W9-AFT-640

The Emergence of Biological Organization

The Emergence of Biological Organization

by Henry Quastler

New Haven and London

Yale University Press, 1964

Designed by Sally Hargrove,
set in Baskerville type,
and printed in the United States of America by
The Colonial Press Inc., Clinton, Mass.

Library of Congress catalog card number: 64-20932

Editors' Note

During the spring term of 1963, the author was Visiting Professor of Theoretical Biology at Yale University. This appointment was part of a program initiated there in the Department of Biology to stimulate interest in theoretical and mathematical approaches to the study of living things. During the previous spring a number of distinguished contributors to these fields, including Dr. Quastler, had lectured at Yale on different aspects of the subject. Most of their lectures will appear in a book entitled *Theoretical and Mathematical Biology* (T. H. Waterman and H. J. Morowitz, eds., Blaisdell, New York, in press).

During those two years a substantial grant from the National Science Foundation (G-21114) made the special courses and visiting lecturers possible. The University and the participating scientific community are grateful for this support and are gratified, too, that some measure of the stimulus and excitement evoked will be extended to a wider audience through publication of the lectures.

The manuscript for this book comprises the revised lecture notes for the second year's course presented by the author. Dr. Quastler worked on rewriting these notes up to the day of his death (July 4, 1963). The material of Chapters I and II is presented here essentially as he left it. Chapter III was in somewhat less polished form and has had more editing. We hope that we have not seriously violated the tone or intent of the original. Dr. Quastler had planned that "a revised version be incorporated into a book on a mathematical theory of biological organization," which he had in mind to develop during the next few years. These beginnings that he has left us are characteristically logical, convincing, and encouraging; they will doubtless be the basis for many exciting developments in our understanding of living systems. Their publication in this little book provides an appropriate tribute to his memory.

We are grateful to a number of people whose assistance has been indispensable, particularly to Dr. Howard J. Curtis for his interest in stimulating the publication of this work in addition to his important biographical and bibliographical contributions to it, to Dr. Harold J. Morowitz for help and advice on many details, as well as to Elizabeth A. Livingston and Barbara W. Folsom, who have greatly aided in editing and preparing the manuscript for the press.

PETER A. STEWART
Department of Biology,
Brookhaven National Laboratory
and
Physiology Department,
Emory University,
Atlanta, Georgia

TALBOT H. WATERMAN
Department of Biology,
Yale University,
New Haven, Connecticut

Henry Quastler

MAY 21, 1908-JULY 4, 1963

Dr. Henry Quastler was a person who endeared himself to all who knew him. He not only had a kindly disposition but a very great intellect; these qualities made him one of the most pleasant and stimulating scientists of the present generation.

He received his M.D. degree in 1932 in his native city of Vienna. After practicing medicine and radiology in Albania for five years, he came to the United States in 1939 and was radiologist at the New Rochelle Hospital until 1942 when he moved to the Carle Clinic in Urbana, Illinois. His inquisitive mind soon led him to the University of Illinois where he quickly made friends and began taking an active interest in research. It was not long before he started an experimental program at the university while he still pursued a full-time medical practice. This was just when high energy accelerators were being developed there, and it was natural that his interests should center on the biological effects of high energy particles. His was some of the first work in this area, and the resulting papers are classic.

In 1949 he finally gave up his medical practice completely and joined the university faculty as a member of the Control Systems Laboratory. Although he had little formal training in mathematics or physics, he was able to master these sciences by himself and made many original contributions in applying them to biology. At that time he was primarily involved in the biological applications of information theory, as well as in maintaining an active experimental program in radiobiology. He was also interested in education and played an important part in the development of biophysics at Illinois.

After a brief stay at Argonne National Laboratory, he joined the staff at Brookhaven National Laboratory in 1956, where he continued a very active research program in radiobiology and mathematical biology with his circle of friends and collaborators growing steadily. The collaborators included not only persons who came to his laboratory to work with him, but those who would visit him for a few days and return home with enough ideas for a year's work.

Henry will be remembered chiefly for his penetrating analysis of the biological effects of radiations. In this work there inevitably emerged a better understanding of biological processes in general. His recent analysis of cell renewal systems in the mammal is an excellent example of this approach. He was always much interested in the application of mathematics to biological problems, and all his work is flavored with it. Those who worked with him absorbed some of his enthusiasm for mathematics, and this may ultimately prove to be his greatest contribution.

His warm heart, his friendly and incisive counsel, and his great enthusiasm for new ideas were the qualities that endeared him to all who knew him.

H. J. CURTIS, Chairman
Department of Biology
Brookhaven National Laboratory
Upton, New York

Preface

This essay is an attempt to develop a theory of biological organization. The theory should eventually include all levels of organization from macromolecules to mammals, but only the first parts have been developed. Even these are unfinished; some well worked-out sections are interlaced with some very sketchy ones. In this sense, these notes should be regarded as a position paper. Putting them down proved helpful to the author and conceivably may prove useful to others.

For individual components of biological systems the problem of organization is one of specification, or information content; this will be illustrated by the question of the specification and development of nucleic acids. With pairs of components different problems arise relating to function, information transmission, action and interaction of information, and the like; these will be discussed in terms of the enzymatic role of proteins. The next level of analysis deals with interactions of actions; it is represented by the interrelations, inside the cell, of nucleic acids which have acquired usefulness by specifying functional proteins. This is as far as the analysis has been carried. Evolution is considered at all levels since evolutionary history is a very important feature of living things.

HENRY QUASTLER

Brookhaven National Laboratory
July 3, 1963

Contents

1

Information

THE BIOLOGICAL PROBLEM

The creative accident. Living things are highly ordered systems—much more elaborately ordered than any known nonliving things. Even the simplest living things show great complexity. In terms of ordered structure the distance between a bacterium and a man is much less than between a bacterium and, say, a giant electronic brain. In the general course of events order tends to give way to less order, and not the other way around; hence it is not easy to see how life could have arisen from nonliving precursors. Several explanations have been proposed, some of which are not subject to scientific inquiry. Of those that are, the most attractive is the proposition that nonliving components have assumed a configuration compatible with life through some lucky accident.

To be compatible with life, a configuration must combine metabolic activity with stability and even adaptability, and it must be able to reproduce itself from available components. This is a big order. To assess its implications we will investigate what seems to be a critical step in the emergence of life: given a "rich, hot, salty sea" containing organic molecules such as amino acids, sugars, polyphosphates, pyrimidines, purines, and so on, what is the probability of an occasion at which a random configuration taken by such molecules is compatible with life? To estimate this probability, two numbers are needed: the probability that any given molecular configuration is compatible with life, and the number of occasions available for forming configurations.

The information content of living things. The large number of molecules needed to constitute a living thing are capable of a vast sum of possible configurations. Among those only a minute fraction seems to be compatible with life. The amount of choice involved in picking a configuration compatible with life out of all the possible configurations can be expressed in terms of information content. Let H be the information content of a structure relative to the ordering of a certain kind of component; then 2^{-H} is the probability of picking at random, from the set of all possible structures of the class considered, one that fulfills the stated criteria. Hence we can examine the probability of any molecular configuration being compatible with life in terms of the information content of living things. Several attempts have been made to estimate, or rather to bracket, the information content of living things. The particular thing here considered will be a relatively simple but self-sufficient organism such as a bacterium. This choice reflects the conviction that once a bacterium exists, all that is needed to achieve the great diversity of presently living creatures is the process of evolution acting over a span of two billion years.

Linschitz (1953) estimated the entropy change inherent in converting simple precursors into the organic molecules which make up the bacterium. Converting entropy into probability, and probability into an equivalent number of binary choices, an information content of 10^{13} bits was calculated. Not contained in this estimate is the specification of macromolecular and cellular structure. On the other hand, only a small fraction of the entropy changes inherent in making up the building stones will find expression in relevant structure, although biologically the latter effect is much more important than the former. Therefore, this estimate is high.

Morowitz (1955) approached the problem on a structural basis. Since it is possible to cool an *Escherichia coli* to near absolute zero without loss of biological activity after rewarming, it follows that the information needed for biological activity must be completely specified by the structure alone; all dynamic coding would be wiped out at near-zero temperature. The information needed to specify the structure is estimated in terms of organic molecules. For each, information is analyzed into the choice of a molecular species and the arrangement of its position with respect to six neighbors where the number of possible relative positions is limited by chemical forces. The information content so obtained is about 10^{12} bits, in good enough agreement with Linschitz. Like Linschitz's, Morowitz's estimate must be high since undoubtedly much of the detailed molecular arrangement in a cell is not relevant to its proper function.

Dancoff and Quastler (1953) developed a number of information estimates based on structure. The information content of any system cannot be greater than the information needed to specify completely the nature and arrangement of all its components. Taking an atom as the simplest component, it is computed how much information is needed to select one atom from the repertory of atoms which make up living matter, and to specify its position within the limits of precision given by thermal vibrations at body temperature; about 24.5 bits per atom will suffice for that purpose. Since an *E. coli* contains about 2×10^{11} atoms, the information content so computed is 5×10^{12} bits. This is an upper bound. It neglects all constraints resulting from the atoms being arranged in molecules. If these constraints are taken into account, the amount of structural information per atom is reduced to about 1×10^{10} bits per bacterium.

All estimates of information content based on structure tend to be high. Much of the structure of a living thing is redundant, and undoubtedly much can be changed without obvious malfunction. It is difficult to estimate just how much of the structure is redundant. A rough assessment of the basic (irreducible) information content can be derived from considering that many of the properties of an organism are the results of the organization of a portion of the whole, the genome. The structural information content of a genome can be reduced to the simplest terms of two bits per nucleotide pair; in the case of a bacterium with about 10^7 nucleotide pairs in its DNA chain, about 2×10^7 bits. This is not yet a lower bound since some of the DNA chain may be redundant and some may be irrelevant (i.e. nonsense DNA). A lower bound of information content is established by considering the functional genetic diversity within a species. This, in a bacterium, needs certainly not less than 1,000 binary contrasts. This yields a low estimate of the information content of a bacterium of 10^3 bits. The brackets thus established—10^3 to 10^{13}—are exceedingly wide but are certain to encompass the true value. A reduction of the width of the limits of estimation would be quite easy, but it is not needed for the present purpose.

An information content of 10^3 bits corresponds to a sequence of 1,000 binary choices or to a single choice among $2^{1,000}$ possibilities. The probability of making such a choice by accident is 10^{-301}. For 10^{13} bits the probability is $10^{-3 \times 10^{12}}$.

Occasions of emergence. The number of occasions for the possible emergence of life through a creative accident is the product of the number of different sites available times the number of occasions the lucky accident could have occurred. The number of sites is the quotient of the total volume available, divided by the volume within which the components of the prospective structure must be confined (overlapping neglected). For an upper bound of the total volume we take the whole surface of the earth (or 5×10^{18} cm^2) covered by water utilizable to a depth of 1 m, a volume of 5×10^{20} cm^3. Surely the minimum volume for the assembly of constituents must be not less than the volume of a bacterium, 10^{-12} cm^3. Thus the number of available sites could not have been larger than 5×10^{32}. To get a lower bound, we assume that only the shores of the ocean provided the interfaces on which an ordering could take place; let the length of the usable shore line be 5×10^{10} cm, i.e. reaching about ten times around the globe. Assume that the unit volume may reach as far as 1 cm in each direction; it could not be much farther if the prospective constituents should reach each other by diffusion without too much delay. The resulting number of sites is 5×10^{10}. We thus find that the number of sites available for the accidental composition of a living structure is between 5×10^{10} and 5×10^{32}—a very crude bracketing which probably could be narrowed down without too much trouble.

The time available for the emergence of life in the "rich, hot, salty soup" full of potential building stones can be estimated as about 2×10^9 years or 2×10^{13} hours. The time available for a single occasion is limited on one side by the speed with which macromolecules and more complex structures are formed, and on the other by the length of time during which incomplete structures can persist pending a possible completion. This minimum time is certainly not less than one hour, the time it takes to form a bacterium from another bacterium under moderately favorable conditions; as an upper limit, one may consider a time 10^{10} times as long, this being a rough estimate of the ratio of reaction rates with and without enzymatic catalysis (Koshland, 1962). This means that on every available site there may have been from 2×10^3 to 2×10^{13} occasions for the creative accident, which could have produced a system with the main features of life.

Multiplying the number of sites (5×10^{10} to 5×10^{32}) by the number of time intervals (2×10^3 to 2×10^{13}) yields the total number of occasions available for the emergence of life: between 10^{14} (the product of the two low estimates) and 10^{46} (the product of the two high estimates), give or take a few orders of magnitude. It would probably not be particularly difficult to reduce the enormous spread of more than 30 orders of magnitude between the bounds of this estimate; however, for the present purpose this is not necessary. It suffices to say that any event of the type considered must have occurred if it has a probability of better than 10^{-10}; and has not occurred except possibly once if it has a probability of less than 10^{-50}.

Conclusions. A very high estimate of the number of occasions available for the building stones (organic molecules) to assemble into a living structure is 10^{46}. A very low estimate of the essential information content of a simple living thing, considered as an ordered arrangement of the same building stones, is 1,000 bits, corresponding to a probability of 10^{-301}. The probability of life having originated through random choice at any one of the 10^{46} occasions is then about 10^{-255}. Using the larger estimate of information content reduces this probability correspondingly. The smallness of this number means that it is virtually impossible that life has originated by a random association of molecules; the proposition that a living structure could have arisen in a single event through random association of molecules must be rejected. Of course, even a virtually impossible event can and will occur once—but not twice. This means that if life should have originated in this utterly improbable manner, then it is certain that no other life of independent origin exists either on earth or anywhere in space; if life of nonterrestrial origin is found on Mars, then the hypothesis of random association of molecules is disproven. At any rate, it is scientifically more rewarding to look for a mechanism that does not call for such a tremendously unlikely accident.

A PREBIOLOGICAL NUCLEIC ACID SYSTEM

Emergence of a nucleic acid system. Various students of the origin of life have considered the transition from organic molecules to organized cellular structure in several steps; the first of these is the formation of macromolecules similar to those found in living things. The first class of macromolecules so considered was the proteins; indeed it has been shown that amino acids can be produced from their constituent atoms by simple physical events, and that amino acids can form protein-like polypeptides (proteinoids) under conditions presumably similar to those in the primeval soup (Miller and Urey, 1959). However, nobody has yet envisaged a mechanism by which proteins formed by accident could be replicated. Since a known mechanism of replication exists for polynucleotides, it is more plausible to consider the possibility that the formation of polynucleotides constituted the first step in the emergence of life.

It can be assumed that the rich, nourishing soup, which presumably existed before living things exhausted the organic molecules present, did contain purines, pyrimidines, sugars, phosphates, and even nucleotides, and possibly triphosphates of the nucleotides. From such building stones, a single-stranded polynucleotide can be produced. This will occur in vitro in the presence of enzymes, and then only rather slowly—about half an hour after the mixture has been prepared. The same reaction unaided by any catalyst may take five million years (assuming the 10^{10} factor mentioned before), but that is not a forbidding requirement since some four hundred such periods were available in the prebiologic period of the earth. Moreover, some inorganic catalysts available at the shores of the sea may have helped polymerization. This whole story is very "iffy"—but the important point is that the formation of a single-stranded polynucleotide is well within the limits of what may have occurred given the available number of occasions. Thus, while the spontaneous formation of polynucleotides is admittedly less probable than the formation of polypeptides, it seems to be sufficiently probable to have occurred on several of the many occasions available. Unlike the proteins, the polynucleotides suggest a number of plausible steps which lead through likely transitions from a macromolecule to a system with a number of near-biological characteristics.

In general, polymerization of a single-stranded polynucleotide is slow, and its hydrolysis fast; thus in a closed system consisting only of nucleotides and their single-stranded polymers, only a small fraction of the available molecules will be polymerized. However, a single-stranded polymer can form a double-stranded one by complementary polymerization, with a single-stranded polynucleotide acting as a template. This process is relatively fast, and the resulting double-stranded polynucleotide is much more stable than the single-stranded because each monomer is bound not only along the sugar-phosphate backbone but also through interstrand bonding between the bases. It is possible that, in the presence of double strands and nucleotides, triple strands may be produced by polymerization along a double-stranded template; or quadruple strands through simultaneous replication of the two members of a double strand (Cavalieri and Rosenberg, 1961; Steiner and Beers, 1961).

A double-stranded polynucleotide can dissociate into two single-stranded ones; conversely, two single strands with largely complementary base sequences can associate into a double-stranded polynucleotide (as shown in the hybrid formation between DNA and the complementary RNA). Also, a triple-stranded polymer can dissociate into a single and a double-stranded one; and vice versa, the two can associate into a triple strand. Thus, once a system contains nucleotides and polymers with complementary base sequences, it will show the following transitions:

single strands associate into double strands
double strands dissociate into singles
double strands are produced by polymerization from single strands and nucleotides
nucleotides are produced by hydrolysis of single strands

Three more transitions—direct polymerization of single and double strands from nucleotides, and hydrolysis of double strands—are comparatively slow and can be disregarded. Adding triple-stranded polymers complicates the picture slightly but does not add any basically new feature, and the same applies for quadruple strands.

So far, the primitive nucleic acid system contains two kinds of single-stranded polymers: one class with a base sequence equal to that originally established, the other with the complementary sequence. The complexity of the system can be greatly increased by the appearance of double strands fused at one end; the fusion can be accomplished by a bridge of three nucleotides (Zubay, 1963). The fusion of chains could be envisaged as following the addition of random monomers after the completion of a complementary polymerization (i.e. beyond the limits of the template chain); or else, in the process of complementary polymerization, a monomer might not pair properly and give rise to a side chain of random monomers which, after doubling upon itself, could then be complemented. There might be other ways of producing fusion between strands. Whatever the cause, the consequences of the existence of a fused double strand will be these: upon dissociation, the molecule formed is a single polymer such that the base sequence of one segment is complementary to the base sequence of the other, except for the three bridging nucleotides. This new type of single-stranded polymer must be capable of hydrolysis, complementary polymerization, and association with a complementary single strand, and in addition, of folding and unfolding (Figure 1).

Stability of a nucleic acid system. A system containing only nucleotides and single-stranded polymers is not self-replicating; if there is a great excess of nucleotides there will always be some single-stranded polymers but they will be random chains differing from each other. It is assumed here and in the subsequent sections that there exists no mechanism which favors the production of particular base sequences. Such mechanisms may exist (Schachman et al., 1960) but no mechanism has been found which *strongly* favors any particular sequence. The presence of some weak preferences would not change the argument given here, which assumes that the first formed base sequences are random, because if some unknown law of polymerization determined the original sequence, whatever this law was, it would find no expression in the subsequent events of

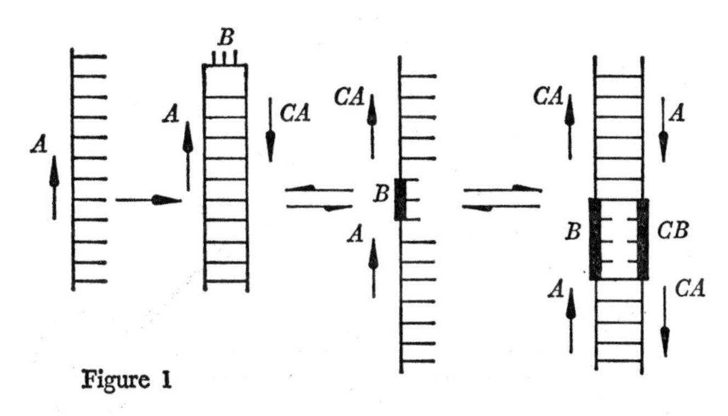

Figure 1

A = Original single strand nucleic acid polymer. The arrows indicate the conventional direction along the chain of the 3′ to 5′ phospho-ester links.
CA = Complementary base sequence in second single strand polymerized on it to form a double strand.
B = "Bridge" of three monomers fusing ends of double strand, which can then unfold to form new single strand, and so on.
CB = Complementary bridge sequence.

complementary polymerization, association, and dissociation. (Note there is a possibility that there exists a particular single strand that polymerizes relatively easily out of building blocks; if this occurs with a frequency comparable to that of producing single strands through dissociation of double strands, then such a system would be obviously stable—indeed could be stable without any recourse to the double strand mechanism. There may be other very special cases: e.g. a strand consisting of a long sequence of G's followed by an equally long sequence of C's will tend to double up upon itself and not dissociate readily, and thus prevent the "1 to 2" complementary polymerization.)

The introduction of complementary polymerization makes possible replication, and also makes the system more stable. Consider a closed system containing nucleotides N, single-stranded polymers P_i consisting of

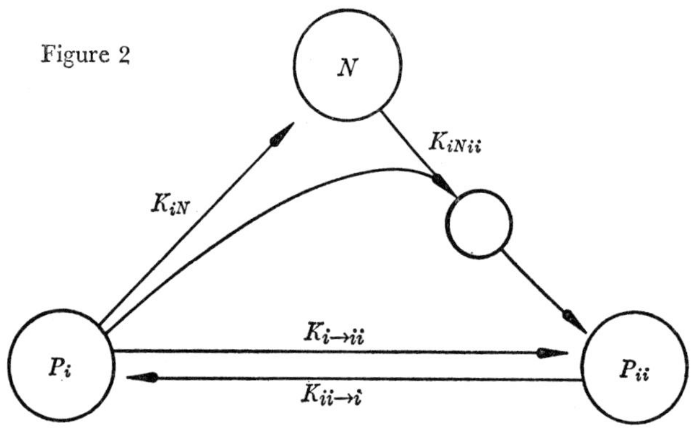

P nucleotides each, and double-stranded polymers P_{ii} (Figure 2). The allowed transitions are as follows:

hydrolysis: $P_i \Rightarrow P \cdot N$ with flux K_{iN} (single strands per unit time)

polymerization: $P_i + PN \Rightarrow P_{ii}$ with flux K_{iNii} (single strands per unit time)

association-dissociation: $2P_i \rightleftharpoons P_{ii}$ with flux $K_{i\to ii}$ and $K_{ii\to i}$ (single strands per unit time)

In the steady state, the fluxes must balance, and we have

for N: $P \cdot K_{iN} = P \cdot K_{iNii}$ hence $K_{iN} = K_{iNii}$
for P_i: $K_{ii\to i} = K_{i\to ii} + K_{iNii} + K_{iN}$
for P_{ii}: $K_{ii\to i} = K_{i\to ii} + 2K_{iNii}$

Consider the fluxes K_{iN} and K_{iNii}. If both are first order in P_i, and K_{iNii} is independent of N, i.e. $K_{iN} = \lambda_{iN}P_i$ etc., then the system will be stable with three components only if $\lambda_{iN} = \lambda_{iNii}$, i.e. if a single-stranded polymer polymerizes or hydrolyzes with exactly equal ease. Otherwise the system will either run out of N or of P_i; the latter uncouples N and P_{ii}. If N, or both N and P_i, is rate-limiting then the system will reach a steady state with three components.

If nucleotides are continuously removed, then the hydrolysis of single strands constitutes irreversible loss to the system. The polymer concentration will run down; however, the rate of decay can be greatly retarded by association into double-stranded polymers. On the other hand, if nucleotides are added in excess, then the polymerization reaction is driven; the polymer concentration grows and, since this furnishes new single-stranded polymers, the excess nucleotides will be used up at an increasing rate. Thus it transpires that the system is stabilized to a degree against fluctuations in nucleotide supply; it will grow or decay only if the supply permanently increases or decreases.

Introduction of triple- or quadruple-stranded polymers increases both the number of stable configurations available, and the possibilities for complementary polymerization. Occurrence of chain fusion with the possibility of a folding–unfolding equilibrium provides still another and possibly very powerful protection against loss of P_i through hydrolysis.

Protobiological systems. The system described has one basic property of living things, self-replication. It does not have a real metabolism, although it does consume building blocks present in the surroundings. The system is mutable since random changes of individual bases may occur and be propagated. Nucleic acid systems may compete with each other for the precursors.

A system that has "hit upon" triple strands, or acquired a foldable chain, is more stable than one which has not gone through these steps and, if it is present in the same space with a limited supply of nucleotide building stones, will out-compete and replace the less complex system. If there is great abundance of nucleotides, then a system with fewer stable states will utilize the material faster and may outgrow a more complex system. It is conceivable that for any set of conditions, largely defined by the supply of nucleotides, there exists an optimum ratio of stable to less stable configurations. Stability depends basically on the number of stable configurations available but can also be modified in a more subtle, gradual way by mutations which affect the ratio of association to dissociation, and folding to unfolding constants. It thus appears that a nucleic acid system is even capable, in a primitive way, of Darwinian evolution.

The argument given is sketchy but it does seem likely that nucleic acid systems would have arisen in the primeval soup of building blocks, and that their emergence would rapidly transform the ambient into the habitat of well-defined and stable molecular systems which compete with each other and exhibit mutability and rudimentary adaptability. It thus seems that an important step in the emergence of biological organization may have occurred without need for a low probability event.

EMERGENCE OF INFORMATION

In the nucleic acid system. The prebiological polynucleotide system depends for its survival on the faithfulness of complementary polymerization. A small or moderate number of errors in making up a complementary strand will not prevent its associating with the template strand or any single strand like it, but errors occurring in successive complementary polymerization will accumulate and then, if the error rate per generation is moderate and high, strands separated by several generations will be sufficiently divergent to make association ineffective. If the unstable single strands cannot readily associate into stable double strands, then the whole system becomes unstable, especially if there is a dearth of building blocks. This does not mean that the error rate has to be zero: it only has to be sufficiently small so that there will be an adequate concentration of equivalent single strands. In this situation, a badly deviant strand will tend to become eliminated since it cannot pair with a normal strand and thereby get stabilized, or else—if it happens to get into favorable circumstances—it may start a new "mutant" system.

Faithfulness of complementary polymerization implies transmission of information: the base sequence of that template strand is preserved through successive complementations, and the only reason why this particular sequence must be faithfully reproduced is just that it happens to be the sequence of the original template strand; a case of conforming for no sake other than conformity's.

For the working of the "prebiological polynucleotide system," almost all base sequences are equally effective. This means that the pattern sequence as such is completely meaningless, i.e. carries no information, is nothing but "noise." This is obviously the case if the original sequence is the result of purely random polymerization; it still applies if the original sequence was lawful in some manner that does not affect the subsequent working of the system. On the other hand, the primarily meaningless sequence acquires very definite meaning as soon as it becomes imperative that it be followed faithfully: information has emerged through the accident of a particular single strand becoming the ancestor of the system, i.e. through the stability properties of the system descended from that particular single strand.

It must be emphasized that the emergence of information out of noise is not the same as the unmasking of information present in noise, e.g. through discovery of a hitherto unknown lawfulness. In the latter case, the information was there, although hidden; in the former, it was not there at all. This is still true if there was some reason for one particular sequence becoming the ancestor of a system: the necessity for faithful complementation would exist even if the choice of the original sequence were completely random. The "accidental choice remembered" is a mechanism of *creating* information and very different in nature from mechanisms of *discovering* information.

Creating new information. The "accidental choice remembered" is a common mode of originating information. Since creation of information is habitually associated with conscious activity, it will be worthwhile to discuss this mode of creating information in terms of human activity. A humble way of originating information furnishes an exact analog to the presumed situation in the case of the nucleic acid system: this is the instance of information emerging by the choosing of a number combination to unlock a safe. It does not matter how the combination was originally selected—wisely, by culling it from a table of random numbers, or unwisely, by using a guessable sequence such as birth date or telephone number. What matters is that before the combination is set into the lock, every number sequence is exactly as good as every other one (namely, no good!), and after it has been set, one sequence is useful and all others are useless. Thus the choice of a sequence and the subsequent implementation of the choice by setting the lock have created information.

On a loftier plane, information emerges when a new work is created by an artist, a composer, a poet. This mode of creating information is based on acts of free will—we know by direct personal experience that man is capable of such feats. By empathy, the capability of having the same experience is granted to beings similar to ourselves. The degree of similarity required may not be the same for everybody, but this is of no great importance. The difficulty arises if we want to deal with this class of events by objective tests, without recourse to empathy. To fix the ideas, suppose we were trying to explain "creation of information through an act of free will" to a strange but articulate and communicative visitor from outer space. If we just point to some creation, the alien will of course note that the supposedly new work is full of rearrangements of patterns which have previously occurred; rearrangements which, moreover, may well follow perfectly established laws. How does one know that at least some new information has emerged or that the new work is more than a rearrangement, according to existing laws, of previously existing patterns? The answer may be in the composer Pierre Boulez's definition of artistic creation: "To make the unpredictable inevitable." To restate this beautifully succinct saying: if there is a truly new element in a work, then it should have been quite impossible to predict this element beforehand, on any basis; if the work is to be successful, then this unpredictable element must acquire the unavoidability of a law. But is not this precisely what happens, in a simple way, each time a new combination is set into a safe lock, and also when a random sequence of bases becomes the ancestor of a nucleic acid system?

It is doubtful whether it is possible to distinguish by objective criteria (as opposed to empathy) between the two modes of originating new information, the accidental choice remembered and the creation through an act of free will. Both lead to unpredictable results. To distinguish randomness from free will, one may have to resort to the consideration of the whole history of an organism: when we make a choice by free will, we do so rationally, which implies profiting from previous experience; whereas the kind of random choice that makes a radium atom disintegrate at a given moment is not apparently controlled by any previous experience of that atom.

The combination of the ability to make unpredictable choices with the ability to learn from experience, and particularly from the results of previous choices, comes as close as we can hope to get to establishing, by objective criteria, the emergence of information through an act of free will. Alas, it has been shown that an automaton could be constructed which very nicely complies with these criteria—without even remotely approximating a situation where empathy suggests itself. The principle of construction is as follows.

One begins with the simplest automaton, an input-output device steered by a program (strategy, code, law), which prescribes what outputs to generate in response to any input in the repertory (see Figure 3). The program may be a very simple one such as: "When you see a green light, go; when the light is red, stop." Or it may involve elaborate computations such as: "Assess the situation which exists following the latest event in the surroundings; consider all possible responses and compute their results as far ahead as you can; assess the resulting situations by analyzing the following list of features . . . computing a value associated with each feature using a given formula with the following parameters . . . and adding up the total expected value for each possible response; choose as output that response for which the expected value is highest." A device operating in this manner may require an elaborate internal structure for the recognition of the input, the generation of the output, and the intervening computation which associates an out-

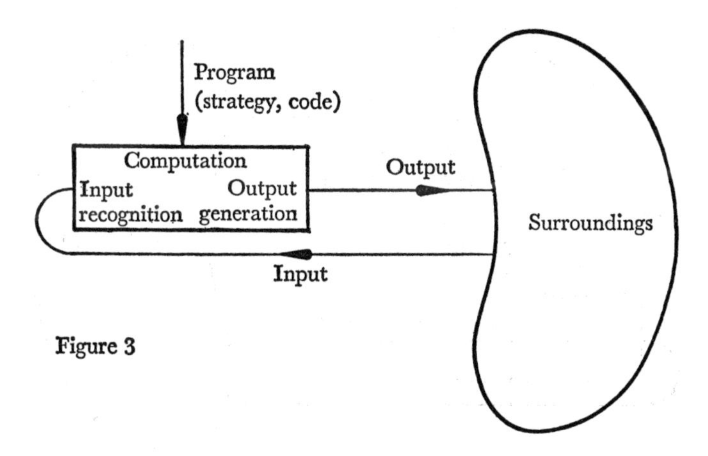

Figure 3

put to an input. Nevertheless, the basic structure of the automaton is still that of a simply programmed input-output device.

The next step in composing the "automaton which generates information through something like free will" consists in replacing the fixed strategy by one that can be adjusted according to completely determined rules. To do this, a strategy computer is introduced, the inputs of which are the cumulative experiences gathered in a series of individual actions, and the outputs the strategy to be used in a future series of actions. Such a device could be structured in a number of ways, e.g. as in Figure 4. The effects resulting from the automaton's output, that is, the actual value of the act, are fed into the memory of the strategy computer, together with the history of the individual acts; after an interval sufficient to collect a representative sample of inputs, the results are compared with the expected values, and the difference, if any, is stored

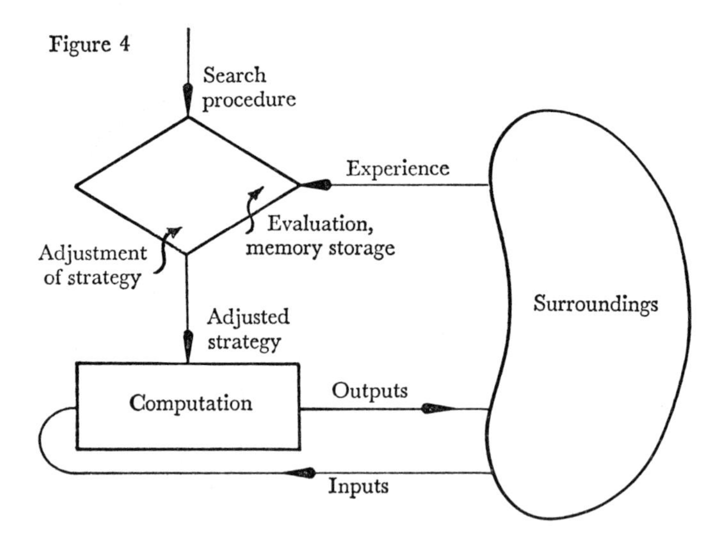

Figure 4

together with a record of the strategy in force. Then the strategy is slightly changed, directly or by modifying one or more parameters used in computing values; the result is assessed; and if it is better than the previous one, additional changes in the same direction are made; otherwise, in the opposite direction.

The automaton clearly "learns from experience." Operating in the manner defined, its strategy computer will explore all strategies which can be found, from the chosen starting point through the prescribed search procedure. It will eventually come to rest at a particular strategy, or keep cycling within a limited number of strategies. It will not necessarily discover the optimum strategy, but it will find one or several that are best within the neighborhood defined. Since surroundings, starting point, and search procedure are given, the results are in principle predictable. If the interval between adjustments is long enough to allow a complete sampling of input-output relations, then even the pathway of the search, or the entire sequence of successive strategies, is in principle predictable. If the automaton is a very complex one, then it may be difficult to predict the result of the strategy search, but this is just a matter of effort.

The final, and critical, step in the conception of the automaton consists in introducing a random element. This can be physically realized in a number of ways; for instance, the device may contain a Geiger counter and a register which simply changes from "1" to "0" and vice versa any time a count is registered. By consulting the register, the automaton can now make random decisions which are unpredictable, provided intervals between consultations of the register are long compared to intervals between changes (Figure 5).

These random decisions have to be used judiciously. An example of an appropriate way is as follows: if, in computing the values of all possible outputs for a given input, a situation occurs where the values of the best and the second-best response are separated by an interval smaller than some given number ε, then the register is consulted; if it indicates "1," the best response is chosen as output; otherwise, the second best. The result of this simple modification is that the automaton is now capable of actions which are truly unpredictable. To be sure, the range of possibilities is not limitless; given a starting point, a search procedure, and a surrounding, it may not be difficult to discover at which point of the search procedure the first random decision will take place, and what its possible outcomes are. The pathway of the search procedure will now show a dichotomy; the two paths originating from this point are again predictable, each one until it reaches a new dichotomy, and so on. The length of pathway between decision points depends on the value

Figure 5

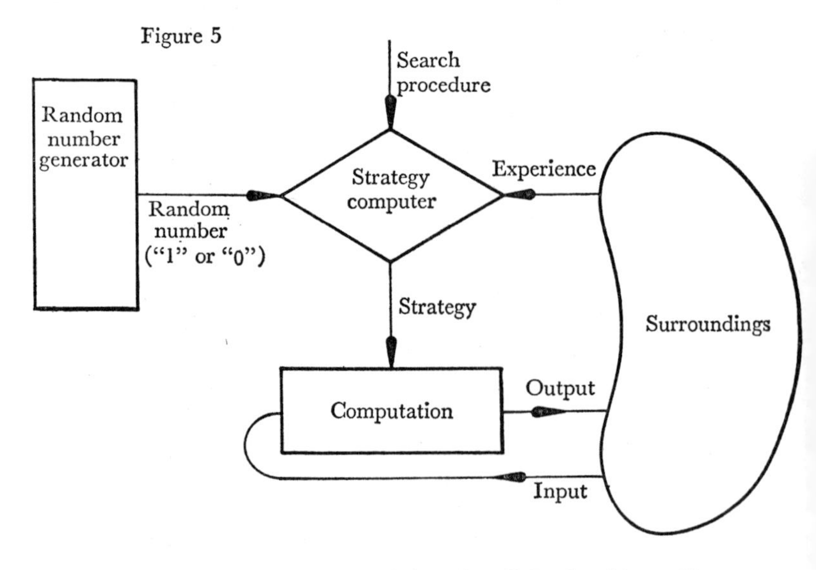

of ε. Unless pathways rejoin, the difficulty in predicting the results of the search procedure increases exponentially with the number of random decisions.

The automaton is now in principle completed; there remains only the minor job of putting together hardware. The automaton is truly capable of unpredictable actions. If the situation is simple enough that the set of all possible outcomes is known, then the range of unpredictability is limited and not disturbing. However, if the situation is such that the set of all possible strategies is either infinite or just much too large to be completely explored (for instance, as is the case for all strategies of playing chess), then the automaton may come up with something that is totally unexpected. Furthermore, it learns from experience, and it uses its unpredictable actions in a judicious way. It will look to us very different from the rational beings endowed with free will that we consider ourselves to be. However, to our rational and communicating visitor from outer space it will not look much stranger than we do, and we may find it difficult or impossible to convince him that we have anything in the way of rationality and free will that the automaton does not have. In producing a good strategy, it has created information; in doing so by means which are unpredictable, it has done something that seems undistinguishable from the creation of information by an act of free will.

It may be fortunate that we have not yet to deal with automata which draw unpredictable conclusions from experience and produce, by means which would not even have to be very complicated, something akin to the noblest act of human consciousness, the creation of new information. This thought may be uncomfortable, but in some ways it is reassuring: it establishes the possibility of the creation of new information, in a manner quite akin to that in which human consciousness operates, by means entirely physical without recourse to vitalistic principles. In other words, it takes the exceptional character out of the process of creating information, and brings it to a level where we may seriously consider the creation of information by an organism much simpler than man, even by a single cell, and even by a prebiological macromolecular system.

2

Information Interaction and the Signature Principle

INTRODUCTION

In the hypothetical prebiological nucleic acid world, the function of a polymer consists in its ability to pair with another strand or to fold upon itself. This function depends on the base sequence of the entire strand, every base contributing to a roughly equal degree. All associations between bases are determined by two simple pairing rules: purine pairs with pyrimidine, 6-keto with 6-amino group. In the world of proteins, the whole style of activities is radically different. Proteins can specifically combine with a vast variety of other molecules, and such combinations depend largely on small fractions of the whole molecule. Thus is introduced a principle of organization which critically affects operations in the protein world while having little importance in the normal functioning of the nucleic acid world. This may be called the Signature Principle (Quastler, 1964). How it operates will be illustrated in two typical instances of enzymatic and hormonal function.

PROTEINS AND THEIR FUNCTIONS

Chymotrypsin. Chymotrypsin is a protein consisting of

242 amino acids of which serine is the most prevalent with 30 residues. Two hundred and twenty-four amino acids have been located, at least tentatively, by sequence analysis. They form three chains which are tied together by several cystine bridges (Bruice, 1962, Hartley, 1962, Koshland et al., 1962).

Chymotrypsin has the enzymatic function of hydrolyzing the *C*—*X* bond:

$$
\begin{array}{c}
\qquad\quad R \\
\qquad\quad | \\
-CO-NH-CH-CO-X
\end{array}
$$

where *X* may be (but does not have to be) the amino group of a polypeptide, and *R* is a benzyl or p-hydroxybenzyl (from phenylalanine or tyrosine).

Tests with enzyme inhibitors (especially the nerve gas DFP), with agents modifying amino acids, and with partial digestion, have produced evidence that this enzyme has two kinds of active site, one for recognition of the substrate, the other for hydrolysis. In the process of hydrolysis by chymotrypsin, one of its 30 serines is critically involved; this is situated on one of the two long chains. One, and only one, of the two histidines was shown also to be critically involved; it is located on the other long chain. The active site for hydrolysis is thus distributed over at least two chains. Significant reduction in the enzymatic activity follows modification of one of the two methionines, presumably one known to be situated three residues away from the active serine (the other is 15 residues away but can be near the active spot if the tertiary structure is right). One of the seven tryptophanes can be chemically modified with resulting reduced activity; the other six are not reactive and are probably buried in the interior of the molecule. An asparagine which is situated near the active serine may be functionally active, particularly since it occurs in the same combination with serine and histidine in two other hydrolytic enzymes; however, another enzyme with similar action has no asparagine in comparable position.

Thus of the 242 amino acids in chymotrypsin, only two (a serine and a histidine) seem to be critically involved in the hydrolysis, with three others (a methionine, an asparagine, and a tryptophane) in important secondary roles; others, such as some cystine groups, may have permissive roles but seem not to contribute to the particular function considered in any specific manner. Some amino acids are definitely known not to be of importance for enzymatic activity; e.g. all the lysine residues can be converted into guanidino groups, which greatly increases their size, without change in enzymatic activity. This does not mean that chymotrypsin consists of *five* essential amino acids and 237 amino acids' worth of garbage; other amino acids may be critically involved in other functions of the protein molecule, including such an enzymatic function as the recognition of appropriate substrate. The important point is that protein molecules are highly differentiated functionally, each function involving some part of the molecule critically and specifically, and other parts only in supporting or permissive roles.

It must be emphasized that we do not understand what constitutes the functional organization of a protein, and that our information on that problem is crude and largely descriptive. To fix the ideas, consider what would happen if a particular function of man, say vision, were studied by methods akin to those used in the functional dissection of enzymes. It might be discovered that a good third of the body could be chewed off, beginning at the toes, before vision was seriously impaired; that the two side chains attached near the other end can be removed without much effect; that chipping at the head abolishes vision pretty soon. Using more subtle methods, a liver or kidney poison would soon show that destruction of these parts will disturb vision, but only after a considerable lag time; hence these parts will be assigned only permissive roles. Some investigator may find a way of cauterizing the whole surface of the structure, including the cornea, and thus find that vision is essentially a surface phenomenon; another may be able to destroy the retina selectively and thus show that intactness of the surface is necessary but not sufficient for vision. It would be discovered that loss of the heart or of the brain stops vision immediately. One can readily imagine the resulting pattern of "active spots" and supporting and permissive regions—and this is just about how we see the functional organization of a protein molecule.

Bradykinin. There occur in nature a number of oligopeptides with specific functions. Among these are the hormones of the posterior pituitary and other substances which affect smooth muscles and vascular tone (kallidins, angiotensin, substance P), substances with effects on nervous transmission, substances which are required for bacterial growth (strepogenin, *Lactobacillus* factor), and many antibiotics. Somewhat larger are the small polypeptides secreted by the anterior pituitary, and insulin. In some of these molecules, the structure–function relation has been checked not only by modification of the natural molecule (as in enzyme studies) but also by synthesis of more or less similar molecules. This yields a different kind of evidence on structure–function relations than could be obtained with modification alone. One of the better studied substances is the hormone *bradykinin* (Whipple and Erdös, 1963).

The blood plasma contains a globulin which when

acted upon by various enzymes yields a 10-peptide which causes dilation of most blood vessels and contraction of some smooth muscles (bronchoconstrictors, intestine, uterus). The peptide is called kallidin (or kallidin II), its precursor kallidinogen, and the peptic enzymes which make the active peptide from the precursor, kallikreins. Kallikreins occur in several organs, and a precursor of kallikrein, in the plasma itself. If kallidin is subjected to tryptic digestion, a lysine is split off, and the remaining 9-peptide, called kallidin I or bradykinin, has about the same activities as kallidin. Further peptic digestion results in inactive oligopeptides. Kallidin and bradykinin are thought to be regulators of local blood flow. The chemical composition of bradykinin, verified by synthesis and bio-assay of the synthetic product, is as follows:

Figure 6

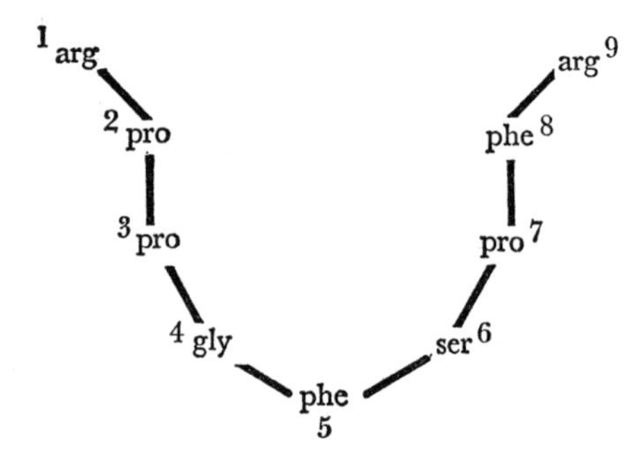

A number of variations of this chemical composition have been tried and tested by bio-assay. In general, activities with various test reactions are found to vary in the same direction but not to the same degree: a given change in the chemical composition will not affect all functions of the molecule in exactly the same way. The following findings were made:

(1) Removal of either 1 or 9 arginine abolishes activity. The cationic character of the two terminal amino acids is not critical: replacement of both arginines by NO_2-arginines, or of one of them by citrilline, lysine, or ornithine results in reduced activity; replacement of both arginines by citrillines leaves no measurable activity.

(2) Removal of proline in position 2 or 3 results in greatly reduced activity; removal of both 2 and 3, or of 7-proline, abolishes activity; replacement of the 7-proline by glycine leaves some activity.

(3) Replacement of the 6-serine by glycine results in no change; replacement by D-serine, in moderate reduction of activity.

(4) If 6-serine is replaced by glycine, the resulting active compound is equal to its retrograde except for 2-proline vs. 6-serine; this difference is critical since a retro-bradykinin is inactive. Yet the phenylalanine can be modified somewhat without effect: p-fluoridation of the phenyl group results in no loss of activity, and replacement by D-phenylalanine, in only moderate reduction.

(5) Replacement of all amino acids 2 to 8 by glycine yields an inactive compound.

Thus bradykinin activity is present within a certain neighborhood of congeners of bradykinin. It is not, however, restricted to this neighborhood: *eledoisin,* a peptide from the salivary gland of a mollusk, of the composition:

H-pyroglutamic-pro-ser-lys-asp-ala-
phe-ilu-gly-leu-met-NH_2

has all tested bradykinin activities to a high degree; yet it has no pair of amino acids in common with bradykinin, it differs in total length, in isoelectric point, and in water solubility (Erspamer and Anastasi,

1962). Two other unrelated peptides, (leu-val-cys-gly-glun-arg-NH_2)$_2$ and (leu-val-cys-isoglu-arg)$_2$, have weak but characteristic bradykinin activities.

The studies with enzymes based on degradation, inhibition, and modification, as well as the studies with smaller peptides based on alternative synthesis, indicate that a particular function is not necessarily associated with a unique molecular configuration. Rather, there exists a certain neighborhood of structurally related amino acid polymers which can perform the same function, although not necessarily with the same efficiency. The bradykinin studies, and similar investigations by Woolley and Merrifield (1963) on bacterial growth factors, have proved that identical functions can be associated with multiple neighborhoods that are structurally unrelated—or, to be more precise, that do not agree in amino acid sequence or in any other way so far studied. This may only mean that the right "language" to describe structure–function relation in proteins has not been found. It could also mean that the functions in question can be elicited through more than one structure.

THE SIGNATURE PRINCIPLE

Definition. Every process involves interaction between entities, in other words, transmission of information. In most real events not all the information content of an entity enters the transmission process, i.e. only a fraction of the features of an entity takes part in a given interaction. This fraction may be called a *signature.*

For example, consider two processes on levels widely separated in the scale of biologic organization: conscious recognition and macromolecular function. A man can recognize a person he knows if he is given a sample of familiar features. Which features are sampled may be imposed by the situation, e.g. if the person is seen at a great distance, or heard over the telephone; in addition, the sample also depends on the habit pattern of the observer's recognition processes. Unless the observer makes a specific effort, he will tend to ignore the difference between an object and its signature; indeed, most people greatly overestimate the amount of information that goes into their recognition processes. Consider the small number of strokes a skillful cartoonist requires to identify a celebrity.

At the macromolecular level, it is clear from the above discussion of chymotrypsin and bradykinin that only a small part of the total amino acid complement of a polypeptide is critically involved in function; this part is the signature. In general, the signature of a molecule consists of all those features which make it a factor in a given reaction; the signature of a macromolecule similarly consists of all monomer arrangements which affect participation in a given reaction. In the nucleic acid world, the signature principle operates on the molecular level as shown by the success of using base analogs; on the macromolecular level, there is little if any evidence of signature operation, all monomers participating to about equal degree in all functional interactions. In the protein world, the signature principle is strongly involved on both the molecular and the macromolecular level: on the molecular level, this is shown by the effect of amino acid analogs; on the macromolecular level, by evidence of the kind described above for the two special cases of chymotrypsin and bradykinin. It is easy to see that the principle of recognition by signatures also works on the levels of cells, cell systems, and physiological functions, in fact on all levels of biological organization.

Before setting down a formal definition of the signature principle, two other closely related concepts need to be discussed: the concepts of a symbol and of the carrier of a signature. A symbol is a signature of the information in a real event, by virtue of some code which may be entirely arbitrary; an operation with a symbol does not necessarily involve the physical intervention of a referent, as when I speak a word. A signature implies the direct presence of the entity, and a carrier of a signature, the direct action of this entity. For instance, an antigenic determinant is the signature of an antigen; an antibody carries the signature but is more than a signature. A substrate is *not* the signature of the enzyme with which it reacts, though it may carry the signature of an enzyme that participated in its production.

In formal terms, let an entity U be a unity with N distinct features, and R_j the range of variation of the j'th feature, where the values w_j within this range may be distinguished qualitatively or quantitatively, and may be discrete or continuous. U can be represented as a vector in N-dimensional space. A signature of U will be a unity V which will contain some, but not all, the information in U. V may be an ordered sample of some of the features of U, in which case it can be represented as a projection of the vector U on some hyperplane with less than N dimensions. It may be an unordered collection of w's. The ranges of the variables represented in V may be less than in U, i.e. some variations of features will not enter the signature although the feature itself will; the features of V may also be the results of operations on some or all the features of U, e.g. the sum of all w's modulo x, or the largest of any w, etc. A *carrier* of a signature will be a unity, some but not all features of which are a signature of U.

Ambiguity and equivocation. Just as a person may have different signatures for different acquaintances, macromolecules have different signatures for different functions. When an entity has two or more functionally different signatures, there will be *ambiguity* of the effect it may cause. On the other hand, significantly different entities may have signatures that are indistinguishable in a given context; there will then be *equivocation* as to the cause of the effect they produce. The convention of using ambiguity for uncertainty of effect, and equivocation for uncertainty of cause, is common in information theory.

Let C be the set of all molecules (or classes of molecules) which make up a given context; let the sub-

Figure 7

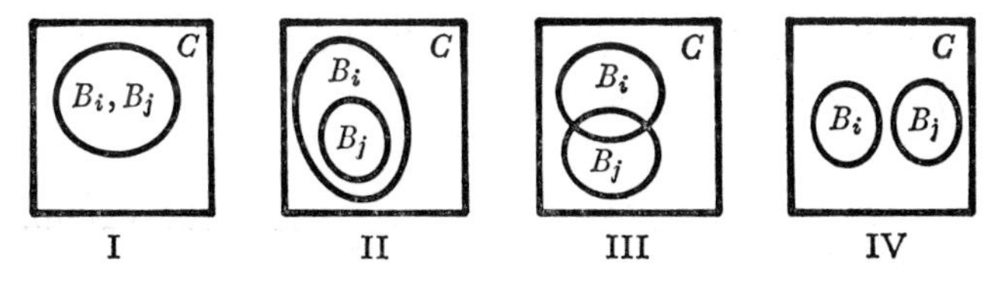

script i denote that a molecule carries a signature enabling it to participate in the i'th reaction in the system; let B_i be the set of all molecules in C carrying the i'th signature. Each molecule may belong to 0, 1, 2, or more B-sets. The molecules belonging to two B-sets, B_i and B_j, may show the following relations (Figure 7):

Case I: All molecules carrying signature i carry also signature j. Result: ambiguity of effects but no equivocation of causes.

II: Ambiguity of effects, limited equivocation of causes (if reaction depending on signature i occurs, the molecule involved may or may not carry signature j).

III: Both ambiguity and equivocation.

IV: Neither ambiguity nor equivocation.

Reliability of signature operation. Overlapping of B-sets causes ambiguity and equivocation. Uncertainty means potential confusion, and confusion of causes or of effects may be harmful. Hence reliability of operation may be expressed as absence of uncertainty. The measure of reliability may thus be related to a measure of the overlap between B-sets. A useful measure can be derived as follows.

Let the context, $\{C\}$, be a set of molecules which participate in a set of reactions through their signatures. For instance, consider all of the protein molecules in a system and the totality of all reactions involving protein molecules which could occur in that system at a given time. The reactions, and therefore the signatures, can be arranged in functional classes (enzymic, antigenic, etc.), whereas the molecules are classified into sets $\{B_i\}$ such that every molecule of $\{B_i\}$ has the signature i. To be computed is the probability that a molecule which belongs to one B-set also belongs to one or more others. If $\{C\}$ is the totality of all molecules, then the probability that a molecule is *not* a member of the set $\{B_j\}$ is $1 - \frac{B_j}{C}$, where B_j, the measure of the set $\{B_j\}$, is the probability that a molecule picked at random is a member of $\{B_j\}$. In this sense, the measure of $\{C\}$ is 1, but it is carried through the calculations explicitly to indicate that the size of B-sets is always measured in relation to the size of the C-set. The probability that a random molecule carries none of the signatures except i is then the product $\prod_{j=1}^{A}\left(1 - \frac{B_j}{C}\right)$ $(j \neq i)$, where A is the total number of signatures in the functional class of interest. A might be the number of different enzyme activities, for example. If A is not too small, and each individual value of B/C is small, then $\left(1 - \frac{B_j}{C}\right) \approx e^{-B_i/C}$ and $\prod_{j=1}^{A}\left(1 - \frac{B_j}{C}\right)$

$\approx e^{-\sum_{j=1}^{A} \frac{B_j}{C}}$ $(j \neq i)$. Now if no single value of B_j contributes very considerably to the sum, then the mean value, $\overline{B}$, is defined by $\frac{(A-1)\overline{B}}{C} = \sum_{j=1}^{A} \frac{B_j}{C}$ $(j \neq i)$ so that the probability that a member of the set $\{B_i\}$ is *not* also a member of another set is approximately $e^{-(A-1)\overline{B}/C}$. The probability that it *is* also a member of some other set is just one minus this value, which for $A > 1$, $A\overline{B} < C$ becomes $\frac{A\overline{B}}{C}$. This is the required number, the probability of uncertainty arising. Note that A measures the functional requirements of the system (e.g. the number of different enzyme activities) whereas $C/\overline{B}$ measures the maximum number of distinguishable signatures, or the functional capacity, A_{max}. Hence the probability of uncertainty arising is given by the ratio of the functional requirements to the functional capacity of the system. This agrees with our intuitive notion that the closer the system is pushed to its limits of capability, the greater the danger of confusion and malfunction.

We will now generalize the above results on equivocation. Let $\{C\}$ be the set of all entities of some class considered in the context. Consider each entity, U, in $\{C\}$ as an ordered array of features. Let there be N such features, the first one with R_1 possible values, the second with R_2, etc. Then each entity is an N-tuple, and the number of possible kinds of N-tuples in $\{C\}$ is the product $R_1 \cdot R_2 \ldots R_N = \prod_i R_i$ $(i = 1, 2, \ldots N)$. But since $R_i = 2^{\log_2 R_i}$, and $\prod_i R_i = 2^{\sum_i \log_2 R_i}$, if we define the mean value of $\log_2 R_i$ by $\sum_i (\log_2 R_i) = N\,\overline{\log_2 R_i}$ then the number of possible kinds of N-tuples in $\{C\}$ is

$2^{N\overline{\log_2 R_i}}$. The amount of information needed, on average, to specify one feature is $\overline{\log_2 R_i}$, provided they are all equiprobable; if they are not equiprobable, we replace $\overline{\log_2 R_i}$ by an information function $H(R_i)$. This involves assumptions about the possibility of reading out coherently whole ensembles of R-values, an assumption probably rarely realized in biological operations; however, this is not critical if the probabilities involved in determining $H(R_i)$ are taken to be some real features of the readout process. Therefore, we let $\overline{\log_2 R_i} = H(R_i)$, and we can write that the information needed to specify an entity U in C is given by $H(C) = N \cdot \overline{\log_2 R_i} = N \cdot H(R_i)$; $H(R_i)$ can also be interpreted as the average amount of information per feature needed in order to specify an entity, U.

Similarly, let functional signatures as well as B-sets be defined by restricted ranges of the features, R_a and R_b respectively. This can mean utilization of only part of the range of variation of every variable, or of all of the range of only some of the variables. Then the number of signatures is $A = 2^{N \cdot H(R_a)}$, and $H(R_a)$ is the average amount of information per feature needed to specify a signature. Similarly, we let $H(R_b)$ be the average amount of information per feature needed to specify a member of a given B-set. Then $H(R_b)$ is also the average equivocation concerning the entity involved when the signature is given, and $H(R_i) - H(R_b)$ represents the reduction in uncertainty concerning the entity involved if the signature is known.

In information theory, this quantity is known as the amount of information transmitted per reaction per single feature; it is denoted by $T(C;A)$. Now the amount of information per feature to be transmitted for successful functioning is $H(R_a)$; the difference, $T(C;A) - H(R_a) = E$ is the excess information per feature, on average, per reaction. Note that excess information is redundant but that not all redundant information is excess information; the signature must contain a certain minimal amount of redundant information to overcome the effects of ambiguity.

Finally we have the probability of equivocation given by $e^{N \cdot E}$. Since this equivocation is derived assuming random selection of members of *B*-sets, it follows that at least as good a result can be achieved with optimal design. With large *N*, random choice becomes a close approximation to optimal design. This shows that if *N*, the number of features integrated in forming the signature, is sufficiently large, the probability of equivocation can be made to vanish as long as there is the slightest amount of excess information in the signature.

The foregoing is a weak statement of the "fundamental theorem of information theory." There are stronger statements of this theorem, showing that the equivocation actually becomes zero (and does not just approximate zero), but these involve elaborate proofs and operations that appear to be beyond the ken of a cell (Shannon and Weaver, 1949).

THE SIGNATURE OF AN ENZYME

Functional requirements. A particular enzyme action involves complex formation with one or more substrates, and catalysis of a reaction. Recognition and chemical action may be dependent on different "active sites" in appropriate geometric arrangement. When an enzyme links two substrates, the two sites may be concerned with the recognition of these substrates, the reaction following automatically upon their apposition. The number of substrates to be recognized in a given cell is a few hundred to, possibly, a few thousand; the number of different actions taken is a dozen or not much more. Such requirements could, in principle, be fulfilled with one to three amino acids (one allows a choice of one in about 20; two, of one in about 400; three, of one in about 8,000).

However, enzymes are made up of building blocks which are large compared to the dimensions of the active site, and the number of stable geometric arrangements of contiguous building stones is very limited. These factors constitute a sort of "quantization noise," which will raise the required number of amino acids per active site. Assuming 15 A as the upper limit of the diameter of an active site, not more than three or at most four amino acids can be accommodated on this area; however, additional amino acids may affect charge distributions, configurations, and ease of changing configurations. These modifying factors will, in general, be less critically specific than the amino acids making up the active site; e.g. glutamic and aspartic acids may be interchangeable in this function. The amino acids responsible for a given function make up the *signature* of the enzyme; they may be grouped close together in the primary sequence, but they may also be scattered and correlated with each other through tertiary structure. The positions on the primary chain which are occupied by the relevant amino acids form an ordered set, or *tuple*.

Enzyme signatures as n*-tuples.* To fix these ideas, consider the tuple responsible for chymotrypsin activity. It contains as critical constituents a seryl and a histidyl residue, located on different chains, i.e. at quite some distance in the primary sequence. A methionyl and a glutamyl residue in the neighborhood of the serine seem to be of secondary importance, i.e. oxidation of the methionine sulfhydryl reduces activity, and the charge of the glutamic acid seems to be of some consequence. Thus it seems that those two members of the tuple are less critically specified; presumably, the glutamyl could be replaced by an aspartyl, or possibly by a neutral amino acid. There also is a requirement that somewhere in the neighborhood one or more disulfide bridges must provide the necessary tertiary structure, and there will be a requirement excluding steric hindrances or strong inappropriate charges in the neighborhood of the active sites, and so on.

As a rough guess, the amino acids involved in the chymotrypsin specificity may form a 20-tuple; it is possible, though, that we are actually dealing with a 242-tuple. The difference is really not so large as it may seem to be at first blush. The point is that only a few members of the n-tuple (whether n be 20 or 242) must be uniquely specified; some members will admit two amino acids, some maybe 10, and some maybe 15. As a result, there will be many tuples with chymotrypsin activity. The overall specificity of the tuple, resulting from the unequal contributions of the several members, is readily computed by information analysis.

Let R be the total number of different amino acids used in building the enzyme (say about 20), and as a first approximation, assume each has equal a priori probability of occurring in any position in the primary amino acid chain. Now let n_1 be the number of positions in the tuple that must be uniquely determined; n_2, the number of positions admitting two amino acids equally well, and so on. Then the information content of a given n-tuple, and therefore of a given signature is $\sum_i n_i \log_2 \frac{i}{R}$ $(n = \sum_i n_i)$, and this quantity may be taken as a useful measure of the enzyme specificity. The generalization to the case where amino acids are not equiprobable, and to the case where some amino acids result in more activity than others, is straightforward and need not be given.

The equivalent k-*tuple*. It will be convenient to represent the n-tuple composed of amino acid positions with more or less stringent requirements by a k-tuple of uniquely specified amino acids. Formally, this means defining

$$\sum_i n_i(\log_2 i - \log_2 R) \equiv -k \log_2 R,$$

$$\text{or} \quad k = N - \frac{\sum_i n_i \log_2 i}{\log_2 R}$$

where the choice involved in specifying all members of the n-tuple is replaced by the selection of the members of a k-tuple, each of which has to be uniquely determined; the uniquely defined k-tuple is thus informationally equivalent to the n-tuple with varying degrees of specificity of the members. By implication, the probability of the uniquely defined k-tuple is the same as that of the average of the original n-tuples, and it is thus permissible to proceed in terms of the uniquely specified k-tuple. The probability that a given k-tuple has just the required unique specification is then simply R^{-k}.

In geometrical terms, the replacement of an n-tuple by an equivalent k-tuple corresponds to a switch from the fuzzily outlined region in n-dimensional C-space to a unit cell in k-dimensional space. Some properties of the C-space may get lost in this transformation. This is illustrated in Figure 8, where two B-sets overlap in two-dimensional space but not in the one-dimensional projection.

The number of amino acids making up a k-tuple is uniquely defined but their nature is not. In general, one will think of a k-tuple as being composed of the critically essential amino acids; e.g. the k-tuple for the hydrolytic activity of chymotrypsin will certainly contain serine and histidine. However, in general there will be no true k-tuple actually capable of performing a given function. The k-tuple is simply a device to overcome the fuzziness of the boundaries of the B-sets

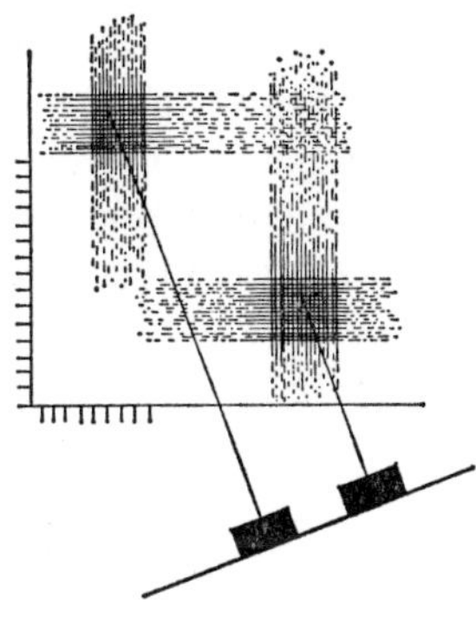

Two B-sets of $n = 2$-tuples in C-space. Density of lines indicates functional activity. The 2 B-sets overlap; there exist molecules with feeble activity in both functions.

Projection onto space of $k = 1$-tuples. Note that the new dimension is not necessarily identical with any dimension in C-space.

Figure 8

formed by n-tuples, where n is not even a well-defined number. The amino acids composing a k-tuple must be considered in a somewhat abstract fashion. Furthermore, the n-tuple and, by implication, the k-tuple approaches are justified to the degree that Crick's (1958) Central Dogma* is valid. If there are only minor deviations (e.g. through ribosomal control of tertiary structure) then the computation will still be essentially correct.

To estimate k, consider the functional requirements spelled out before. Several modifiers that allow some leeway in specificity are equivalent to a small number of critically specific amino acids. Whatever the value

* "This states that once 'information' has passed into protein *it cannot get out again.* In more detail, the transfer of information from nucleic acid to nucleic acid, or from nucleic acid to protein may be possible, but transfer from protein to protein, or from protein to nucleic acid is impossible. Information means here the *precise* determination of sequence, either of bases in the nucleic acid or of amino acid residues in the protein" (Crick, 1958, p. 153).

of N, a value $k = 2$ is barely sufficient functionally, and 7 is amply so. Then the probability of a given signature (k-tuple) is between 20^{-2} and 20^{-7}, or with slightly narrower limits, and changing to base 10, between 10^{-3} and 10^{-6}. In other words, the specificity of an enzyme like chymotrypsin, defined in terms of its signature, implies an amount of information per molecule between 10 and 20 bits, compared to a total information content per molecule, considered as a random chain of about 240 amino acids, of over 1,000 bits.

THE EMERGENCE OF A COMPLETE SET OF FUNCTIONS

Conditions for emergence. Consider the following problem: what is the probability that a randomly formed amino acid sequence will contain all the signatures needed to fulfill a given number of requisite enzymatic functions? It is known that protein-like coacervates, "proteinoids," can be made to arise under laboratory conditions set up to resemble the primeval soup (Fox, 1960). It is obvious that complete systems must be found if either the amino acid sequences available are tremendously long, or if the number of occasions for the formation of a system is tremendously large—this is simply the principle by which a member of the Grand Academy of Lagado is producing a complete body of every statement that can be made. The problem is whether a sequence of plausible length will contain with a reasonable probability everything that is needed.

A protein system as described above will not replicate, at least not by any known mechanism. It is imaginable though that such a system could perpetuate itself. If among the enzymatic functions represented are those needed to elaborate amino acids from material present, to gain energy from available fuel, and to facilitate the formation of (random) polypeptides, then the whole complex may keep going and indeed exhibit protobiological features such as primitive metabolism, competition for food with other systems in the same space and, through competition, some evolution.

A critical step in the evolution of the modern system is a linkage between a nucleic acid system and a protein system in a kind of symbiosis, made possible through the emergence of the ribosomal apparatus. We have no theory concerning this event—too much is known about the ribosomal apparatus to permit superficial models, and not enough to permit setting up very detailed ones. We will only observe, somewhat lamely, that an enzyme system good enough to perform some 100 functions ought to be good enough to provide the makings of a ribosomal apparatus.

Since they do not compete for the same material, nucleic acid systems and "proteinoid" systems could coexist in the same neighborhood. If any pair of nucleic acid and protein systems hit upon a ribosomal mechanism and thus established a symbiotic relation, it would immediately have a great competitive advantage and crowd out all other systems. Thus the accident of choice, of a particular pair integrating into a single system, would make the results of the accident inevitable, simply by removing the conditions for a like accident to happen again.

Requirements and size. Consider a set of required functions F_i, $i = 1, 2 \ldots A$. If the F's are enzymatic functions, then A must be at least 100. A function can be performed by a B-set of n-tuples; each set will be represented by a single k-tuple. Let β_i = probability that a randomly chosen k-tuple fulfills F_i. For simplicity's sake, let $\beta_i = \beta$ for all i's (β was estimated above to be between 10^{-3} and 10^{-6}). Consider a set of C k-tuples, randomly chosen, and estimate the probability that a set of C-tuples, randomly selected, will have at least one tuple for each function F_i.

If β is the probability of a random tuple having a given function, then $b = \beta \cdot C =$ the expected number of k-tuples with a given function in a set of C k-tuples. (Note that b is the number of exactly equal k-tuples, and differs from B, the set of all n-tuples equivalent to a given k-tuple.) Then $e^{-b} =$ the probability of a C-set *not* containing at least one tuple with the required property, and

$$(1 - e^{-b}) = \text{the probability of containing at least one such tuple.}$$

Then, the probability of emergence of a complete set, P_E, is

$$P_E = (1 - e^{-b})^A = \text{probability of a } C\text{-set containing at least one tuple of every one of the } A \text{ required kinds.}$$

In order to evaluate this probability, we must obtain a plausible estimate of the quantity b, and therefore of C.

Effective length of an amino acid sequence. Since a hybrid system of nucleic acid and polypeptides should crowd out any system not so linked, we will consider only the effective number of tuples which can be linked to, or coded by, an amount of nucleic acid found in the simplest organisms capable of independent life. These contain 10^5 to 10^8 nucleotide pairs, and can therefore code amino acid sequences of about one third this length. Assume 10^7 as a representative value for the maximum number of amino acids that can be coded.

A protein with a total of C amino acids could have as many as C potential locations of k-tuples if every position could serve as base. Actually, the number is smaller. Any n-tuple equivalent to a given k-tuple will extend over a total length L_k of the primary chain; this will not make a large difference if C is very large, but if the total protein is divided up into m separate pieces (of length $\frac{C}{m}$) then the available number of positions will be

$$m\left(\frac{C}{m} - L_k\right) = C - mL_k.$$

To assess this end-effect, consider a total protein of size $C = 10^7$ amino acids. If the functional protein molecules contain about 300 amino acids, then $m \simeq 3.10^4$; L_k may be as much as half the length of the polypeptide, or 150; hence $ml \simeq 4.5 \cdot 10^6$, or about $0.5C$. Furthermore, not all amino acids are accessible; a fraction is buried within the interior of the protein molecule. (Note that accessibility may change in the course of the reaction by the Induced Fit Mechanism [Koshland, 1963].)

To get a rough idea of the magnitude of the accessibility factor, consider the following: let a large cube be made up of small cubes, a small cubes to the edge. Then the little cubes *not* reaching the surface form a large cube of edge $(a - 2)$, and the number of cubes making up the surface of this large cube is:

$$a^3 - (a - 2)^3 = 8 + 6a^2 - 12a.$$

In a cube made out of 125 little cubes, 98 or 78% reach the surface; with 1,000 little cubes, the number is 488. Hence if proteins were roughly cubical structures, about 50 to 75% of the amino acids should be accessible at the surface. This estimate could be high by a factor of two if one considers not the whole amino acid but only its residue; it is certainly biased, since in an aqueous medium hydrophilic residues will tend to be at the surface and hydrophobic residues in the interior; on the other hand, the estimate is low, since the shape of proteins is more complex than a simple cube. Altogether, an accessibility factor of one half may not be too unrealistic.

End effects, accessibility, and other factors will tend to make the *effective* size of a given collection of amino acid chains about 0.1–0.01 of the actual length. Thus C may be between 10^5 and 10^6.

Estimation of emergence probability. We can now put in some rough estimates of actual numbers. We have for β, $10^{-3} > \beta > 10^{-6}$, with 10^{-4} as the most likely value. The effective size of C for a bacterium may be 10^5–10^6, with 10^6 probably high. Hence $b = \beta C$ should be bracketed between 10^3 and 10^{-1}, but the lower limit of b cannot be less than 1, so that for b we have $1 < b < 1{,}000$, with the most likely value between 1 and 10. P_E was shown to be $(1 - e^{-b})^A$, and we estimated A at 100. This results in the following values for P_E:

$$\begin{array}{llll} \text{If } b = 10 \text{ or more,} & P_E = 0.99 \rightarrow 1.0 \\ \quad b = 5 & P_E = 0.5 \\ \quad b = 1 & P_E = 10^{-20} \end{array}$$

These numbers suggest that the probability of obtaining a complete set of enzymes by coding proteins from 10^7 nucleotide pairs may be quite high.

3

Organized Systems and Gene Interactions

INTRODUCTION

It was conjectured that the primitive nucleic acid system showed little or no functional differentiation between individual segments of the polynucleotide chain. However, once the system became coupled with a protein system, then a particular part of the polynucleotide chain acquired a particular usefulness by virtue of being responsible for a particular functional protein. In other words, a chain of nucleotides becomes a system of genes without necessarily suffering any change in structure or in reaction patterns. Distinctions between sense, nonsense, and missense arise in the context of function and are basically irrelevant in the nucleic acid domain.

So far as discussed in the preceding chapter, the gene functions are associated rather than organized, each gene specifying a protein without regard to the activities of other parts of the nucleic acid system. Only with the introduction of feedback from the protein domain into the nucleic acid system can there be interaction between the functions of genes, and thus organized function. In other words, the organization of gene functions depends on the transmission to the nucleic acid system of information relating to the results of its activities.

NUCLEIC ACID ACTIVITIES IN CELLS

List of activities. Some and possibly all cellular functions of nucleic acids can be interpreted in terms of the elementary operations of the prebiological system: hydrolysis, complementary polymerization, association, and dissociation.

(1) *Replication* of DNA and direct replication of RNA involve polymerization and dissociation. $P' + NP \Rightarrow P''$, where $P', P'' \ldots$ represent polynucleotides and P single nucleotides. N is an integer.

(2) *Template-dependent production* of RNA involves polymerization and dissociation. $P'' + NP \Rightarrow P''' \Rightarrow P'' + P'$.

(3) *Decay:* hydrolysis $P' \Rightarrow NP$.

(4) *Specification of amino acid sequence:* association-dissociation (between messenger and transfer RNA).

(5) *Association of messenger RNA with ribosomes:* its nature is not known; since the relation is nonspecific, it is probably of the same nature as the association between nucleic acids and polymerases.

An activity that may or may not be mediated by nucleic acids is specific repression and derepression of individual portions of the genome. If this process is carried out by nucleic acids, then it involves specific association and subsequent dissociation. Since the repressing agent is diffusible it should be an RNA (provided it is a nucleic acid at all); the other strand may be the messenger RNA of the repressed gene, or the DNA itself, either the template or a complementary strand serving in the mechanism of release of messenger RNA (Paigen, 1962).

(6) *Repression:* association, $2P' \rightleftharpoons P''$ or $P'' + P' \rightleftharpoons P'''$.

(7) *Derepression:* dissociation $P''' \Rightarrow P'' + P'$ or $P'' \Rightarrow 2P'$.

The difference between the hypothetical "prebiological" system and the modern one is that most of these operations are now enzymatically catalyzed. The relation between nucleic acids and enzymes is largely nonspecific, in the sense of not depending on the specificity of a particular base sequence; otherwise it must be highly structured, as indicated by the facts that in vitro complementary polymerization replicates many, but not all, features of the in vivo process, that DNA and RNA synthesis seem to compete for the template, and that the presumably high selectivity of base pairing in protein synthesis (between messenger RNA and transfer RNA) cannot be explained on the basis of Watson-Crick pairing alone.

States of DNA. If it is true that the foregoing list comprises all nucleic acid activities, then genetic DNA should always be in one of the following five states:

(1) Replicating DNA, through complementary polymerization catalyzed by DNA polymerase.

(2) Making RNA, through complementary polymerization catalyzed by RNA polymerase.

(3) Dynamically repressed, by specific association with repressor RNA.

(4) Statically repressed; this condition is simply postulated in view of the fact that in the cells of higher organisms most genes are inactive most of the time, a situation that it would be very wasteful to achieve by dynamic repression.

(5) Free, following completion of (1) or (2) or derepression through dissociation; this may be assumed to be a highly unstable (transient) state.

The following transitions are likely to be common:

(1 → 5) = completion of replication (dissociation)
(2 → 3) = repression (association)
(3 → 2) = derepression (dissociation)
(4 → 2 or 1) = gene activation (mechanism?)
(3 or 5 → 1 or 2) = initiation of replication of transcription (mechanism?)

States of RNA. RNA occurs in three different compartments: hybridized with DNA, free, and ribosome-bound. In addition, being more labile than DNA, it is in equilibrium with a pool of precursors. The scheme of Figure 9 shows the states, the transitions, and the nucleic acid functions involved in them:

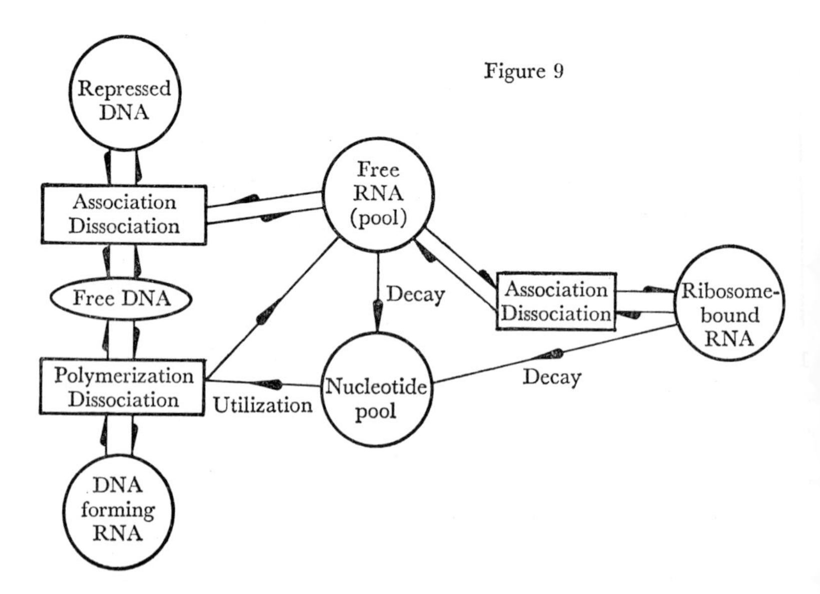

Figure 9

This scheme contains all elements needed to account for that portion of the control of gene activity that is confined within the nucleic acid world. The only complication that will be introduced is that some RNA molecules will have to interact with genes other than those which served as their templates.

ACTION OF THE NUCLEIC ACID DOMAIN ON THE PROTEIN DOMAIN

It is widely believed—and we concur—that nucleic acids affect the protein world only by specifying amino acid sequences in protein synthesis, and that this specification completely determines the structure and func-

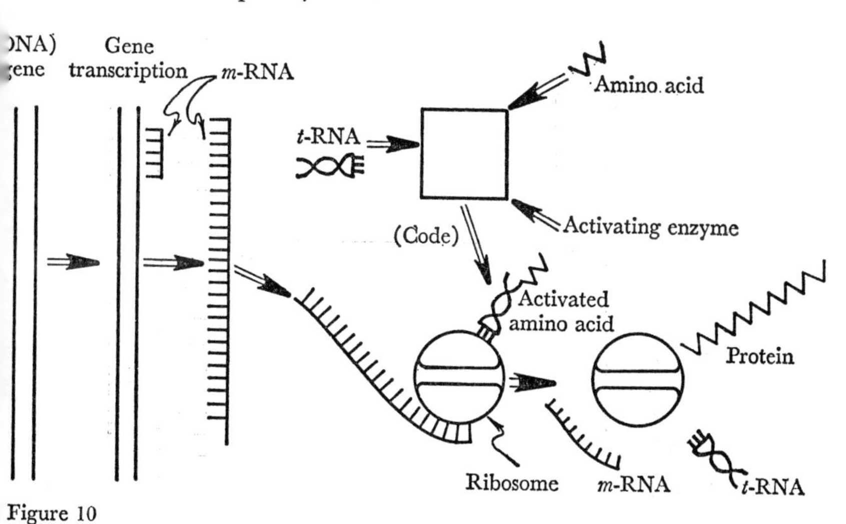

Figure 10

tions of proteins. The process of transmission of information involves a considerable number of steps: the transcription of information on the DNA sequence to messenger RNA (m-RNA); attachment of messenger RNA to a ribosome and translation of the base sequence into an amino acid sequence according to a nucleic acid–protein code (Figure 10). The physical embodiment of the code is a collection of activated amino acids which are molecules of soluble or transfer RNA (t-RNA) complexed with amino acids, the linkage having been mediated through specific activating enzymes (Zubay, 1963).

A discussion of the specific theories involved is not needed here, but one point will be of importance in the subsequent discussion: while the m-RNA and the protein it specifies are necessarily informationally related, there is no reason to believe that the physical similarity between the members of such a pair is significantly greater than that between any kind of protein and any

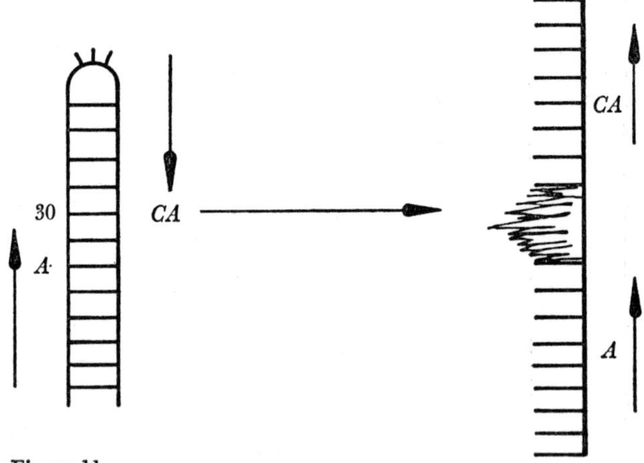

Figure 11

kind of m-RNA—that is, very slight. They are not informationally equivalent since the RNA–protein code is degenerate. The RNA completely specifies the protein, but not vice versa.

If the molecular model of t-RNA as given by Zubay is correct, then it has interesting cell biological or evolutionary implications. The model assumes that a good fraction of the 67 nucleotides making up the molecule forms a double helix; this implies that the unfolded molecule has two stretches about 30 nucleotides long which are complementary, as indicated in Figure 11.

It has been shown that t-RNA specifically hybridizes with DNA. This means one of two things: either the DNA acts as template for only one of the two complementary stretches, the other being produced by RNA polymerizing with RNA as template—which, if true, is an interesting item of cell biology; or else, the DNA itself must contain stretches such that one is complementary to the other. We shall see what this implies. The probability of a random occurrence of such a constellation, at the right interval, is 4^{-30} or 10^{-18} which is small and remains small, namely 10^{-9}, when we relax the conditions to postulate that only half the bases must pair properly. This is a low, but not impossibly low, probability. However, if it is assumed that at least 18 t-RNA are coded independently and should have arisen independently, then the joint probability for this is 10^{-162} which is impossibly low. The necessary conclusion is that either these stretches of DNA have arisen independently from folded stretches (see Chapter I, pp. 10-15), or that they are multiple representatives of the same original sequence (which itself might well be the result of folding), secondarily modified by mutations.

ACTION OF THE PROTEIN DOMAIN ON THE NUCLEIC ACID DOMAIN

Regulator, operator, and structural genes. In the protein domain, the activity pattern is controlled by the results of activity; a number of purely passive mechanisms assure a certain degree of stability; also, enzymes are inhibited by the products of their own activity, some by the products of enzymes several reaction steps removed. These controls are rapid and highly flexible but of limited effectiveness, since they leave the protein composition of the system unchanged. Slower but more profound effects can be achieved by regulating the production of protein through intervention in the nucleic acid domain—at the level of the gene, through interference with messenger synthesis, interference with messenger release or, finally, blocking of messenger action. It has become established, largely due to the work in bacteria of Jacob, Monod, and their associates (1961), and of McClintock in maize (1961), that such actions exist and are controlled by specific genes. These genes are called regulator genes; they control the amount of an enzyme as distinct from the structural genes which control its amino acid composition and thereby its specific structure and function. It is known that regulator genes act through diffusible substances. It is also known that their activity is controlled by substances of the general class of metabolites. Hence the line of communication and control from the outer world into the nucleic acid domain is supposed to go from the general metabolic pool to the regulator gene and from there to the structural gene, which elicits production of the enzyme, which in turn affects the chemical composition of the metabolic pool. Thus the feedback loop is closed.

The communication link from cytoplasm to structural gene includes two recognition processes involving diffusible substances: specific reaction between repressing agent and inducer or co-repressor, and between repressing agent and structural gene. Both reactions can be used to draw inferences on the nature of the repressing agent. We consider first the reaction between repressing agent and structural gene. There is some evidence (Jacob and Monod, 1961) that this reaction does not involve the structural gene directly but is mediated through a portion of the genome called the *operator gene,* which is contiguous with one or more structural genes that are transcribed as a unit. It may be that the operator gene locally controls initiation of RNA synthesis.

RNA as repressor agent. The primary product of a regulator gene, like that of every gene, is presumably an RNA molecule. It could be that this itself is the repressor agent. This conjecture is supported by the finding (Pardee and Prestidge, 1959) that the repressor for β-galactosidase can be formed in the presence of the inhibitors of protein synthesis, chloramphenicol and 5-methyl-tryptophane. This mechanism involves correspondence between base sequences of regulator and regulated genes. We consider two possibilities: the repressing agent is an RNA of some size, say from 20 nucleotides up, or else it is an oligonucleotide. In the former case, combination with the target gene could occur through hybridization without need for enzymatic catalysis; the requirements for specificity are easily fulfilled since a sequence of 20 nucleotides is not likely to be found twice in a string of 5×10^7 nucleotide pairs (it takes 13 nucleotide pairs to raise the chance to 50% that the sequence occurs at least twice). This implies events such as folding or duplication in the evolution of the nucleic acid chain since the probability of the random occurrence of a number of regulator-operator pairs, under this hypothesis, is much less than 10^{-50}.

Suppose the repressing agent is an oligonucleotide. The minimum number of nucleotides needed to yield the requisite variety depends on the number of repressible genes: it may be estimated that, in *E. coli,* this number is not less than 100 and probably not more than 1,000. Now, four nucleotides can make up 256 different ordered sequences, five, 1,024, and six, 4,096. This means that a small sequence, or a small portion of an RNA molecule, could suffice in principle to provide specific reactions with all operators available. This mechanism imposes no constraints on the genesis of the DNA chain; in a sequence of 5×10^7 nucleotides, any given tetranucleotide can be expected to occur about 2×10^5 times, a hexanucleotide, about 10^4 times. By the same token, this mechanism involves severe constraints on the differentiation between operators and other parts of the genome, since otherwise the oligonucleotide would form almost nothing but nonfunctional hybrids; furthermore, the hybridization of a short sequence must be enzyme-mediated to be highly specific.

Assuming that the repressor molecule is an oligonucleotide implies stringent requirements on the structure surrounding the DNA chain in the cell; assuming that it is a long RNA molecule imposes requirements on the evolution of the DNA chain. In either case, an additional agent is needed to explain the specific reaction with inducer or co-repressor since nucleic acid molecules are not known to combine specifically with anything but other nucleic acids. The natural choice for a mediating agent is a protein enzyme. This requires that there exist A enzymes, $100 < A < 1{,}000$, each of which recognizes inducer or repressor or both on one hand, and a polynucleotide on the other. Enzymes of this kind of double specificity are known to exist, namely the activating enzymes. There is a difference, though, in that the activating enzyme must correctly associate one of 18 (or more) amino acids with one of 18 (or more) classes of RNA, or one pair out of 324 to about 500 possible pairs; on the nucleotide side, this involves recognition of a triplet which is probably sufficiently redundant to be almost (Quastler and Zubay, 1962), or quite (Roberts, 1962), reducible to a doublet. For the repression mechanism, the enzyme has to select one pair in 10^4 to 10^6 possible pairs and, in doing so, to recognize a sequence of four to six nucleotides. This is more specificity than any known enzyme possesses. At this point we consider this problem only in terms of its evolutionary implications.

Paigen (1962) has postulated that messenger and repressor (or "censor") RNA both act as templates in protein synthesis, and that the proteins they specify react both with some substrates and with the templates themselves. This is possible, but in view of the nature of the encoding mechanism there seems to be no reason at all why a protein once removed from the ribosome should react more readily with its template RNA than with any other RNA. We will, therefore, investigate the possibility that a given enzyme happens to carry, by chance, a tuple of amino acids which enables it to react with the RNA that served as its template. Let this probability equal $\beta \times$ the number of available tuples per molecule; we may bracket it between 10^{-2} and 10^{-5}. If the system contains several enzymes of the required substrate specificity, then only one of them must also react with its template; the number of such enzymes may be between 1 and 10, and the probability that at least one of them recognizes its template is then bracketed between almost 10^{-1} and 10^{-5}.

But in a system with 100 to 1,000 repressible genes there must then be the same number of enzymes with the required double function. This means that for every complete set of enzymes (in the sense specified before, of performing A functions), the chance is 10^{-3} to 10^{-8} that it will have the enzymes needed to react with repressor RNA and with inducers and co-repressors. This probability must be reduced by approximately another three orders of magnitude, since besides recognizing the proper substrates the enzymes must also activate or inactivate the RNA, depending on whether the other molecule involved is an inducer or co-repressor. The resulting probability of emergence by accident is on the order of 10^{-6} to 10^{-11}, which is small but not impossibly so. The probability of an enzyme system being complete was estimated to be between 1 and 10^{-20}, and the product of the two probabilities is in the range from 10^{-6} to 10^{-30}. As stated before, probabilities greater than 10^{-50} may not be completely negligible.

Protein as repressor. Since an enzyme is needed to mediate between the cytoplasm and the nucleic acid domain, one may ask whether this enzyme itself could not be the repressor. The regulator gene could form a messenger RNA, which acts as template for an enzyme with the following properties: if complexed with, or activated by, a co-repressor, it reacts with the operator in a way to block the gene activity; reaction with an inducer inactivates the enzyme and thus blocks inhibition of the operator. This would include the repressor among the allosteric proteins (Monod et al., 1963). The information difficulties are the same as discussed before.

The following genetic evidence has been adduced in support of the protein nature of the repressor agent (Garen and Garen, 1963). R_1 and R_2 are mutants in *E. coli* which change alkaline phosphatase from an inducible to a constitutive enzyme; they are due to mutations of regulator genes. Both are suppressed by the suppressor mutation *su,* i.e. in the presence of *su,* alkaline phosphatase becomes again an inducible enzyme even though R_1 or R_2 are present. The locus of *su* is distant from the loci of R_1 and R_2. The suppressor *su* also suppresses other mutations (Benzer and Champe, 1962; Garen and Siddiqi, 1962) in a way which seems to indicate that *su* affects the encoding mechanism for protein synthesis and indeed makes protein synthesis possible in certain cases where it had been blocked by a mutation. It was argued that since *su* permits protein synthesis in some cases where this has been impossible because of mutations, and since *su* restores regulation which had been abolished by the mutations R_1 or R_2, the agent of regulation ought to be a protein.

Suppression by RNA as a result of protein synthesis. The repressor can be produced when protein synthesis is blocked; therefore it is a nucleic acid. Repression is restored in repressionless mutants by a suppressor, which re-establishes the lost capability of synthesizing a protein; therefore the repressor agent is a protein. Neither conclusion is necessarily valid (and was not presented to be so), and both involve the organizational difficulty of requiring a large number of allosteric proteins with precise specificity for a nucleotide sequence and another molecule, the former having specificity greater than in any known cases. A model previously proposed (Quastler, 1963) circumvents these difficulties as follows: it is assumed that the regulator gene produces a messenger RNA which, through base sequence correspondence, can associate with the operator, or the structural gene, or its product RNA, and thereby produce repression. However, the m-RNA can also connect with a ribosome and cause the synthesis of a protein. This protein must be able to react with inducer and repressor *before* it is pulled off the ribosome: reaction with co-repressor liberating the RNA, possibly by pulling off a finished protein, and reaction with inducer resulting in an antimetabolite-like reaction with blocking of the whole structure. The RNA so immobilized will eventually be hydrolyzed. This proposed mechanism accounts for the known facts:

(1) Genetic DNA, under proper conditions, will produce messenger RNA unless specifically blocked.

(2) The RNA produced by the regulator gene may have different functions, but one of them is to hybridize with the operator or structural gene, blocking RNA

synthesis, or else with the messenger RNA, blocking its function (Yanagisawa, 1963).

(3) An association-dissociation equilibrium exists between repressing RNA and the inhibited DNA or messenger RNA, hence the amount of gene activity varies inversely with the amount of repressor RNA.

(4) The level of repressor RNA, at a constant rate of production (it is conceivable that the production rate itself can be regulated by other genes) depends on the association-dissociation equilibrium and on the rate of hydrolysis of free RNA, but most of all on the fate of ribosome-bound repressor RNA: if this is immobilized by inducer, the level of free RNA falls, and when the co-repressor effect dominates, it rises.

(5) The finding that repressor can be produced in the absence of protein synthesis would indicate that in this case repressor RNA does not attach to the ribosome, or is released without protein synthesis.

(6) The restoration of repression lost by the R-mutations through the suppressor *su* could be interpreted as follows: the repressor RNA produced by the mutant gene attaches to a ribosome and begins protein synthesis but cannot finish it, the RNA remaining stuck as in the presence of inducer; the *su* effect allows the synthesis of the protein to go through and thus restores the normal situation.

In this model no molecule is supposed to do anything but its ordinary activities: nucleic acid reacts with nucleic acid, and protein with substrate; the difficult informational link between protein and RNA is replaced by a mechanical link which is not specific and requires no information. It is implied that there is no basic difference between repressor RNA and messenger RNA, although some genes may be specialized in providing RNA mostly usable in one function or the other.

One may ask, why does not r-RNA block the regulator gene and, in the same line, why does not m-RNA itself block the structural gene? The answer is that it may well do so; the effectiveness of RNA production would then depend on the relative rates of association and dissociation between RNA and genetic DNA on one hand, m- or r-RNA and ribosomes on the other. The substrate of an enzyme could act as co-repressor and block further production—a kind of feedahead control which may work well.

A molecule of m-RNA (or r-RNA) in the pool can go three ways: it can attach to a ribosome with probability p_R, or it can decay, or it can associate with DNA with probability p_D. The magnitude of p_R can be estimated as follows: let X be the number of protein molecules specified per m-RNA (or r-RNA); assume that after each protein synthesis the m-RNA is detached from the ribosome, and that the decay of ribosome-bound RNA can be neglected. Then the expected value of X will be $p_R(1 - p_R) + 2\,p_R^2(1 - p_R)$ $+ \ldots = (1 - p_R)\sum_i i \cdot p_R^i = \frac{p_R}{1 - p_R}$, hence

$$p_R = \left(\frac{X}{X + 1}\right).$$

In log-phase *E. coli*, X is about 5–10, hence p_R is about 0.83 to 0.91; in reticulocytes where X is large, p_R must be very nearly equal to 1. This is assuming that the hypothesis that m-RNA is detached after protein synthesis holds. (In the reticulocyte there is no known way of replacing lost m-RNA; of course, it may stop making hemoglobin as it runs out of m-RNA.)

Let:

p_R/p_D = (number of effective available ribosomes) $\times$ (reaction constant)/(effective number of available DNA sites) $\times$ (reaction constant).

Now the number of available DNA sites may be one, two, or a few; the number of ribosomes is about 10^5 in *E. coli;* the number of available ribosomes probably is 10^2–10^4. This suggests a value p_D of about 0.01. If for each RNA molecule which associates with a DNA, about 90 link with a ribosome, and if travel times are short compared to times of binding, then there will be about 90 ribosome-bound RNA molecules for each DNA-bound one, under the scheme of dynamic repression–derepression. This means that 50 to 150 ribosomes may be involved in the repression process for each repressible gene locus. There may be 100 to 1,000 repressible gene loci, which means that in *E. coli* between 5,000 and 150,000 ribosomes could be tied up in dynamic repression. Since this organism has about 10^5 ribosomes, the indication is that a very considerable fraction of them might be tied up in dynamic repression; this is compatible with the fact that only a minor fraction (1–10%) is active in protein synthesis.

In the higher organism with many more genes to be repressed and with evidence that some repressions become irreversible during differentiation, the dynamic repression–derepression mechanism is much less likely, since it would tie up too many ribosomes. Besides, this mechanism takes place in the cytoplasm, and in higher organisms genes are sequestered in the nucleus.

The model here given is compatible with Zubay's idea (Zubay, 1964) linking the rise in antibody formation following antigen stimulation with derepression. He postulates that the antibody acts as a repressor of the gene which specifies the antibody; the repressor is removed by combination with antigen, and increased production is permitted. All we have to postulate to accommodate the principle to our model is that the antibody acts as the co-repressor of the gene which specifies it; this will release messenger RNA to reassociate with the gene, yielding self-inhibition as previously described. The antigen, in combining with antibody in process of formation, would immobilize the complex including messenger RNA and thus act as an inducer.

Figure 12

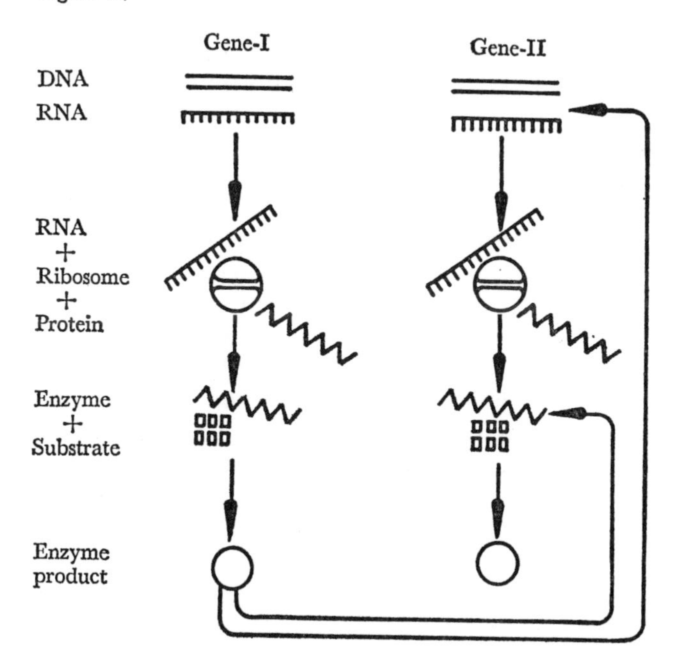

Coordinated gene function. A Gene-I can affect another Gene-II at a number of levels: (1) the I-RNA it produces may inhibit production of II-messenger RNA through association with II-DNA, or block protein synthesis by association with II-messenger RNA itself; (2) the I-protein specified by I-RNA may remove or produce substrate for the II-protein; (3) the product of the I-protein may act as inducer or co-repressor of the Gene-II, or as inhibitor of protein-II. A third gene, III, can affect Gene-II indirectly by operating on Gene-I.

The mutual control of the gene system can thus be effected using only the primitive nucleic acid activities, without direct information transmission from the outer world, not knowing, as it were, the effects of these activities in the protein domain. The only condition is that some pairs of genes, which interact through association of strands, can produce enzymes which are related in that the substrate of one corresponds to the inducer or co-repressor of the other. Under normal conditions, the substrate of an enzyme tends to be similar to its inducer, and the co-repressor similar to its product. This only means that structurally similar nucleic acids specify enzymes that are functionally related—at least often enough to allow the development of a repression–derepression control system. The proposition that like RNA can specify enzymes with like function does not contradict the statement previously made that there is little, if any, specific physical similarity between an enzyme and its template.

Genes interact through correspondence of base sequences. Since we do not know how accurate the correspondence must be, we cannot speculate whether it may or may not be due to accident. We have raised this problem several times, and always concluded that the likely mechanism behind correspondence in the genome is evolution, including replications and foldings.

There is another feature, this one in the protein domain, which adds more credence to this assumption. End product inhibition is a common feature in enzyme systems, and it is thought to be largely allosteric, i.e. depending on two different active sites (Monod et al., 1963). This means that one enzyme in a series of about 5 to 10 must contain two sites of related though different specificities. The probability of having a particular site, in addition to the one already carried, is $\beta \times$ the number of available tuples in a protein molecule, say, about 15×10^{-4}; the probability of having such combination at least once in 10 possible candidates, about 1.5×10^{-2}—but the probability of having such arrangement in each of about 100 enzyme systems, 1.5×10^{-4} or less. This is an admissible probability—yet the explanation that such functional relations between enzymes are due to structural relations between base sequences is more attractive.

If the modern nucleic acid system did evolve through chain fusion, doubling, and subsequent diversification through base changes (Freese, 1962), then such a history should be expressed in partial repetitions of amino acid sequences within and between proteins; this occurs not infrequently (Lanni, 1963).

In discussing the emergence of a set of functions, the emergence of the ribosomal apparatus was taken for granted and no attempt was made to explain it. A similar omission was made implicitly in the discussion of the emergence of an organized system of functions, namely the emergence of an enveloping membrane. Dynamic control in a system with some 10^4 genes and 10^5 ribosomes as described is possible only if the whole system is enclosed within a small volume by a membrane. The limiting size of the system is defined by the time it takes an RNA molecule to find a DNA with which it can associate. Hence the great diversity seen at the present time, combined with dynamic control, must have evolved *after* the system was enclosed.

References

Benzer, S., and S. D. Champe, 1962. A change from nonsense to sense in the genetic code, *Proc. Natl. Acad. Sci. U.S., 48:* 1114–1121.

Bruice, T. C., 1962. Intramolecular catalysis and the mechanism of chymotrypsin action, *Brookhaven Symp. Biol., 15:* 52–84.

Cavalieri, L. F., and B. H. Rosenberg, 1961. The replication of DNA, *Biophys. J., 1:* 317–352.

Crick, F. H. C., 1958. On protein synthesis, *Symp. Soc. Exptl. Biol., 12:* 138–163.

Dancoff, S. M., and H. Quastler, 1953. The information content and error rate of living things. In: *Information Theory in Biology* (H. Quastler, ed.), pp. 263–273, Univ. Illinois Press, Urbana.

Erspamer, V., and A. Anastasi, 1962. Structure and pharmacological actions of eledoisin, the active endecapeptide of the posterior salivary glands of eledone, *Experientia, 18:* 58–59.

Fox, S., 1960. How did life begin? *Science 132:* 200-208.

Freese, E. E., 1962. On the evolution of the base composition of DNA, *J. Theoret. Biol., 3:* 82–101.

Garen, A., and S. Garen, 1963. Genetic evidence on the nature of the repressor for alkaline phosphatase in *E. coli, J. Mol. Biol., 6:* 433–438.

Garen, A., and O. Siddiqi, 1962. Suppression of mutations in the alkaline phosphatase structural cistron of *E. coli, Proc. Natl. Acad. Sci. U.S., 48:* 1121–1127.

Hartley, B. S., 1962. On the structure of chymotrypsin, *Brookhaven Symp. Biol., 15:* 85–100.

Jacob, F., and J. Monod, 1961. Telenomic mechanisms in cellular metabolism, growth, and differentiation, *Cold Spring Harbor Symp. Quant. Biol., 26:* 398–401.

Koshland, D. E., Jr., 1962. The comparison of nonenzymatic and enzymatic reaction velocities, *J. Theoret. Biol., 2:* 75–86.

Koshland, D. E., Jr., 1963. Biological specificity in protein-small molecule interactions. In: *Proc. 1st Intern. Pharmacol. Mtg., 7:* 161–191, Pergamon Press, N.Y.

Koshland, D. E., Jr., D. H. Strumeyer, and W. J. Ray, Jr., 1962. Amino acids involved in the action of chymotrypsin, *Brookhaven Symp. Biol., 15:* 101–133.

Lanni, F., 1963. Analysis of sequence patterns in ribonuclease III: Variable-span pair-order analysis, *J. Theoret. Biol., 4:* 1–27.

Linschitz, H., 1953. The information content of a bacterial cell. In: *Information Theory in Biology* (H. Quastler, ed.), pp. 251–262, Univ. Illinois Press, Urbana.

McClintock, B., 1961. Some parallels between gene control systems in maize and in bacteria, *Am. Naturalist, 95:* 265–277.

Miller, S. L., and H. C. Urey, 1959. Organic compound synthesis on the primitive earth, *Science, 130:* 245–251.

Monod, J., P. Changeux, and F. Jacob, 1963. Allosteric proteins and cellular control systems, *J. Mol. Biol., 6:* 306–329.

Morowitz, H. J., 1955. Some disorder-order considerations in living systems, *Bull. Math. Biophys., 17:* 81–87.

Paigen, K., 1962. On the regulation of DNA transcription, *J. Theoret. Biol., 3:* 268–282.

Pardee, A. B., and L. S. Prestidge, 1959. On the nature of the repressor of β-galactosidase synthesis in *Escherichia coli, Biochem. Biophys. Acta, 36:* 545.

Quastler, H., 1963. Chemical communication systems in the cell, *Trans. N.Y. Acad. Sci., 25:* 382–395.

Quastler, H., 1964. General principles of systems analysis. In: *Theoretical and Mathematical Biology* (T. H. Waterman and H. J. Morowitz, eds.), Blaisdell, N.Y. (in press).

Quastler, H., and G. Zubay, 1962. An RNA-protein code based on replacement data. II. Adjustment and extension, *J. Theoret. Biol., 3:* 496–502.

Roberts, R. B., 1962. Alternative codes and templates, *Proc. Natl. Acad. Sci. U.S., 48:* 897–900.

Schachman, H. K., J. Adler, C. M. Radding, I. R. Lehman, and A. Kornberg, 1960. Enzymatic synthesis of deoxyribonucleic acid. VII. Synthesis of a polymer of deoxyadenylate and deoxythymidylate, *J. Biol. Chem., 235:* 3242–3249.

Shannon, C. E., and W. Weaver, 1949. *The Mathematical Theory of Communication,* 117 pp., Univ. Illinois Press, Urbana.

Steiner, R. F., and R. F. Beers, 1961. *Polynucleotides,* 404 pp., Elsevier, Amsterdam, The Netherlands.

Whipple, H. E., and E. G. Erdös, eds., 1963. *Structure and Function of Biologically Active Peptides, Ann. N.Y. Acad. Sci., 104:* 1–464.

Woolley, D. W., and R. B. Merrifield, 1963. Anomalies of the structural specificity of peptides, *Ann. N.Y. Acad. Sci., 104:* 161–171.

Yanagisawa, K., 1963. Genetic regulation of protein biosynthesis at the level of the ribosome? *Biochem. Biophys. Res. Commun., 10:* 226–231.

Zubay, G., 1963. A molecular model for protein synthesis, *Science, 140:* 1092–1095.

Zubay, G., 1964. Regulation of gene action, *Science* (in press).

Bibliography of Henry Quastler's Scientific Publications

1930 Quastler, H., and H. Weingarten, Koennen Fische ihre Riechschleimhaut regenerieren? (Regeneration of the nasal mucosa in fish), *Arch. Entwicklungsmech. Organ., 122:* 763–769.

1931 Spiegel, E. A., and H. Quastler, Experimentelle und klinische Untersuchungen Blut-Liquor-Schranke (Influence of X-rays and diathermy on the hemoencephalic barrier, *Wien. Med. Wochschr., 81:* 1059–1061.

1932 Quastler, H., Steigerung der Messgenauigkeit bei Messung kleinster Sichtbarer Grössen mit dem Schraubenmikrometerokular (Increased precision in microscopic measurements), *Z. Wiss. Mikroskopie, 49:* 195–207.

1936 Quastler, H., Ueber den Aggregatzustand der Erythrozyten (The physical state of erythrocytes), *Wien. Klin. Wochschr., 49:* 244–245.

1937 Hoche, O., and H. Quastler, Zur Diagnostik und Therapie abgekapselter intrapulmonarer Tumoren (Intrapulmonary tumors), *Arch. Klin. Chir., 188:* 567–578.

Quastler, H., Die Wirkung herdferner Bestrahlungen in der Röntgentherapie tuberkulöser Lymphome (Indirect irradiation in the X-ray therapy of tuberculous lymphomas), 1st Congr. Austrian Radiol. Soc., *Strahlentherapie, 58:* 688–693.

Quastler, H., Erfahrungen mit der Niedervolttherapie auf Hautkrebsen (Low voltage therapy of skin cancers), *Strahlentherapie, 59:* 182–185.

1942 Chilko, A. J., and H. Quastler, Delayed metastases in cancer of the breast, *Am. J. Surg., 55:* 75–82.

Quastler, H., Roentgenoscopic localization of foreign bodies, *Am. J. Roentgenol. Radium Therapy Nucl. Med., 48:* 107–109.

1943 Quastler, H., Depth dose measurements in contact roentgen therapy on a biological test object (rabbit's skin), *Am. J. Roentgenol. Radium Therapy Nucl. Med., 50:* 669–676.

1945 Austin, V. T., and H. Quastler, Idiopathic (?) hypoprothombinemia, Report of a case, *Am. J. Med. Sci., 210:* 491–500.

Quastler, H., Note on cholecystography with Priodax: Dosage and gastrointestinal effects, *Radiology, 45:* 190–191.

Quastler, H., Studies on roentgen death in mice. I. Survival time and dosage, *Am. J. Roentgenol. Radium Therapy Nucl. Med., 54:* 449–456.

Quastler, H., Studies on roentgen death in mice. II. Body weight and sensitivity, *Am. J. Roentgenol. Radium Therapy Nucl. Med., 54:* 457–461.

Quastler, H., and R. K. Clark, Biological evaluation of 20 million volt roentgen rays. I. Acute roentgen death in mice, *Am. J. Roentgenol. Radium Therapy Nucl. Med., 54:* 723–727.

1946 Quastler, H., The use of the betatron in cancer therapy: A preview, *Cancer Res., 6:* 483–484 (Abst.).

Vestling, C. S., S. Kaufman, R. E. Maxwell, and H. Quastler, The oxidation of octanoate by normal and leucemic mouse liver homogenates, *J. Biol. Chem., 165:* 385–386.

1947 Chase, H. B., H. Quastler, and L. S. Skaggs, Biological evaluation of 20 million volt roentgen rays. II. Decoloration of hair in mice, *Am. J. Roentgenol. Radium Therapy Nucl. Med., 57:* 359–361.

Quastler, H., Remarks about the application of the betatron in cancer therapy, *Illinois Med. J., 91:* 119–122.

Quastler, H., Possibilities of the betatron in cancer therapy, *Sci. Education, 31:* 9–11.

Quastler, H., and R. K. Clark, Evaluation biologique des rayons-X à 20 millions de volts (mort des souris par des rayons-X pénétrants), *J. Radiol. Electrol. Med. Nucl., 28:* 469–472.

1948 Adams, G. D., H. Quastler, et al., Techniques for application of the betatron to medical therapy, *Am. J. Roentgenol. Radium Therapy Nucl. Med., 60:* 153–157.

Quastler, H., and M. Baer, Inhibition of plant growth by irradiation. I. Discrete steps of growth inhibition and pattern of dose-response-relation, *J. Cellular Comp. Physiol., 31:* 213–234.

1949 Kirschner, L. B., C. L. Prosser, and H. Quastler, Increased metabolic rate in rats after X-irradiation, *Proc. Soc. Exptl. Biol. Med., 71:* 463–467.

Luce, W. M., H. Quastler, and L. S. Skaggs, Biological evaluation of 20 million volt roentgen rays. III. Recessive sex-linked lethals in *Drosophila melanogaster, Am. J. Roentgenol. Radium Therapy Nucl. Med., 62:* 555–558.

Quastler, H., The biologic effects of high energy roentgen rays, *Intern. Cancer Res. Congr. 4th St. Louis (1947), 6:* 825–830.

Quastler, H., Studies on radiation death in mice, *Cancer Res., 9:* 552.

Quastler, H., et al., Techniques for application of the betatron to medical therapy, with report of one case, *Am. J. Roentgenol. Radium Therapy Nucl. Med., 61:* 591–625.

Quastler, H., and M. Baer, Inhibition of plant growth by irradiation. II. Sensitivity and development, *J. Cellular Comp. Physiol., 33:* 349–363.

Vestling, C. S., J. N. Williams, Jr., S. Kaufman, R. E. Maxwell, and H. Quastler, The oxidation of octanoate by liver homogenates from leucemic mice, *Cancer Res., 9:* 639–644.

1950 Luce, W. M., H. Quastler, and E. F. Lanzl, Biological evaluation of 20 million volt roentgen rays. V. Bar effect in *Drosophila, Am. J. Roentgenol. Radium Therapy Nucl. Med., 64:* 963–967.

Quastler, H., Radiotherapy of acne vulgaris: Comparative tests of treatment technics, *Radiology, 54:* 247–255.

Quastler, H., and M. Baer, Inhibition of plant growth by irradiation. III. Successive radiation effects; homologous responses, *J. Cellular Comp. Physiol., 35:* 75–94.

Quastler, H., and M. Baer, Inhibition of plant growth by irradiation. V. Radiation effects on initiation and completion of growth, *Cancer Res., 10:* 604–612.

Quastler, H., and E. F. Lanzl, Biological evaluation of 20 million volt roentgen rays. IV. Efficiency and dosage range, *Am. J. Roentgenol. Radium Therapy Nucl. Med., 63:* 566–574.

Thomas, L. J., and H. Quastler, Preliminary report of X-ray effects on the nematode *Rhabditis strongyloides, Science, 112:* 356–357.

1951 Luce, W. M., H. Quastler, and H. B. Chase, Reduction in facet number of bar-eyed *Drosophila* by X-rays, *Genetics, 36:* 488–499.

Quastler, H., Acute intestinal radiation death, *Federation Proc., 10:* 106 (Abst.).

Quastler, H., E. F. Lanzl, M. E. Keller, and J. W. Osborne, Acute intestinal radiation death. Studies on roentgen death in mice, III, *Am. J. Physiol., 164:* 546–556.

1952 Osborne, J. W., H. S. Bryan, H. Quastler, and H. E. Rhoades, X-irradiation and bacteremia. Studies on roentgen death in mice, IV, *Am. J. Physiol., 170:* 414–417.

Quastler, H., A. M. Schertiger, and W. N. Stewart, Inhibition of plant growth by irradiation. IV. Growth arrest vs. effects on mitotic activity. *J. Cellular Comp. Physiol., 39:* 357–369.

1953 Austin, M. K., J. S. Laughlin, and H. Quastler, Relative biological effectiveness of 17 MeV electrons, *Brit. J. Radiol., 26:* 152–153.

Dancoff, S. M., and H. Quastler, The information content and error rate of living things. In: *Essays on the Use of Information Theory in Biology* (H. Quastler, ed.), pp. 263–273, Univ. Illinois Press, Urbana.

Quastler, H., The measure of specificity. In: *Essays on the Use of Information Theory in Biology* (H.

Quastler, ed.), pp. 41–71, Univ. Illinois Press, Urbana.

Quastler, H., The specificity of elementary biological functions. In: *Essays on the Use of Theory in Biology* (H. Quastler, ed.), pp. 170–188, Univ. Illinois Press, Urbana.

Quastler, H., Feedback mechanisms in cellular biology. In: *Cybernetics, 9th Conf.* (H. von Foerster, ed.), pp. 167–181, Josiah Macy Foundation, New York.

1954 Quastler, H., and A. A. Blank, *Notes on the Estimation of Information Measures,* 36 pp., Report No. R-56, Central Systems Laboratory, Univ. Illinois, Urbana.

1955 McGill, W. J., and H. Quastler, Standardized nomenclature: An attempt. In: *Information Theory in Psychology* (H. Quastler, ed.), pp. 83–92, Free Press, Glencoe, Ill.

Quastler, H., Approximate estimation of information measures. In: *Information Theory in Psychology* (H. Quastler, ed.), pp. 124–139, Free Press, Glencoe, Ill.

Quastler, H., Information theory terms and their test psychological correlates. In: *Information Theory in Psychology* (H. Quastler, ed.), pp. 143–171, Free Press, Glencoe, Ill.

Rose, F. C., H. Quastler, and S. M. Rose, Regeneration of X-rayed salamander limbs provided with normal epidermis, *Science, 122:* 1018–1019.

1956 Austin, M. K., M. Miller, and H. Quastler, Five- to eight-day radiation death in mice, *Radiation Res., 5:* 303–307.

Bourgin, R. C., R. Krumins, and H. Quastler, Radiation-induced delay of pupation in *Drosophila, Radiation Res., 5:* 657–673.

Quastler, H., Studies of human channel capacity. In: *Information Theory* (C. Cherry, ed.), pp. 361–371, Academic, New York; Butterworths, London.

Quastler, H., The nature of intestinal radiation death, *Radiation Res. 4:* 303–320.

Quastler, H., *A Primer on Information Theory,* 66 pp., Office of Ordinance Research, Ordinance Corps, U.S. Army, Durham, N.C.

Quastler, H., Modes of acute radiation death, *Peaceful Uses of Atomic Energy, 11:* 121–124.

Quastler, H., M. K. Austin, and M. Miller, Oral radiation death, *Radiation Res., 5:* 338–353.

1957 Quastler, H., The complexity of biological computers, *IRE Trans. Electron. Computers, 6:* 192–194.

Quastler, H., Labyrinth damage by X-irradiation, *Radiation Res., 7:* 444 (Abst.).

1958 Anslow, W. P., Jr., H. Quastler, et al., The use of mathematics in biology; summary of a group discussion. In: *Homeostatic Mechanisms, Brookhaven Symp. Biol., 10:* 259–262.

Hughes, W. L., H. Quastler, et al., Cellular proliferation in the mouse as revealed by autoradiography with tritiated thymidine, *Proc. Natl. Acad. Sci. U.S., 44:* 476–483.

Jaroslow, N., and H. Quastler, Antigenic specificity. In: *Symposium on Information Theory in Biology* (H. P. Yockey, R. L. Platzman, and H. Quastler, eds.), pp. 211–217, Pergamon, London.

Lewis, Y. S., H. Quastler, and G. Svihla, Ultraviolet microscopy of x-irradiated intestine, *J. Natl. Cancer Inst., 21:* 813–823.

Quastler, H., A primer on information theory. In: *Symposium on Information Theory in Biology* (H. P. Yockey, R. L. Platzman, and H. Quastler, eds.), pp. 3–49, Pergamon, London.

Quastler, H., The domain of information theory. In: *Symposium on Information Theory in Biology* (H. P. Yockey, R. L. Platzman, and H. Quastler, eds.), pp. 187–196, Pergamon, London.

Quastler, H., Information theory in radiobiology, *Ann. Rev. Nucl. Sci. 8:* 387–400.

Quastler, H., F. G. Sherman, G. Brecher, and E. P. Cronkite, Cell renewal, maturation and decay in the gastrointestinal epithelia of normal and irradiated animals, *Peaceful Uses of Atomic Energy, 2nd Intern. Conf., Geneva, 22:* 202–205.

Sherman, F. G., G. Brecher, E. P. Cronkite, and H. Quastler, DNA synthesis, cell duplication and migration in the small intestine of normal and irradiated mice, *Federation Proc., 17:* 148 (Abst.).

1959 Cronkite, E. P., H. Quastler, et al., Dynamics of hemopoietic proliferation in man and mice studied by H^3-thymidine incorporation into DNA. In: *Progr. Nucl. Energy, Ser. VI, Biol. Sci.* (Proc. 2nd Intern. Conf. Peaceful Uses of Atomic Energy, Geneva, 1958; J. G. Bugher, J. Coursager, and J. F. Loutit, eds.), *2:* 92–105, Pergamon, New York.

Quastler, H., Storage and actuation of genetic information: the information theory approach, *Lab. Invest., 8:* 480–494.

Quastler, H., Information theory of biological integration, *Am. Naturalist, 93:* 245–254.

Quastler, H., Cell renewal and acute radiation damage, *Radiology, 73:* 161–165.

Quastler, H., Some aspects of cell population kinetics. In: *The Kinetics of Cellular Proliferation* (F. Stohlman, ed.), pp. 218–222, Grune and Stratton, New York.

Quastler, H., The description of steady-state kinetics. In: *The Kinetics of Cellular Proliferation* (F. Stohlman, ed.), pp. 431–433, Grune and Stratton, New York.

Quastler, H., Preface. In: *Proc. 1st Natl. Biophysics Conf., Columbus, Ohio, 1957* (H. Quastler and H. J. Morowitz, eds.), pp. vi–viii, Yale Univ. Press, New Haven.

Quastler, H., Quality of radiation and selectivity of biological effects. In: *Proc. 1st Natl. Biophysics Conf., Columbus, Ohio, 1957* (H. Quastler and H. J. Morowitz, eds.), pp. 704–714, Yale Univ. Press, New Haven.

Quastler, H., J. P. M. Bensted, L. F. Lamerton, and S. M. Simpson, Effects of dose-rate and protraction: A symposium. II. Adaptation to continuous irradiation: Observations on the rat intestine, *Brit. J. Radiol., 32:* 501–512.

Quastler, H., and F. G. Sherman, Cell population kinetics in the intestinal epithelium of the mouse, *Exptl. Cell Res., 17:* 420–438.

Quastler, H., and M. Zucker, The hierarchy of modes of radiation death in specifically protected mice, *Radiation Res., 10:* 402–409.

1960 Cattaneo, S. M., H. Quastler, and F. G. Sherman, DNA synthesis in irradiated hair follicles of the mouse, *Radiation Res., 12:* 587–593.

Hampton, J. C., and H. Quastler, Some observations on radiation damage in epithelial cells of the mouse intestine. In: *Proc. Intern. Conf. Electron Microscopy, 4th, Berlin, 1958* (W. Bargmann, D. Peters, and C. Wolpers, eds.), *2:* 480–484, Springer, Berlin.

Lipkin, M., T. P. Almy, and H. Quastler, Stability of protein in intestinal epithelial cells, *J. Clin. Invest., 39:* 1007 (Abst.).

Quastler, H., Introduction to symposium on theoretical radiobiology, *Am. Naturalist, 94:* 57–58.

Quastler, H., Radiation effects *in vivo:* Molecular aspects of mammalian radiobiology. In: *Bioenergetics, Radiation Res., Suppl. 2:* 627–638.

Quastler, H., Cell population kinetics, *Ann. N.Y. Acad. Sci., 90:* 580–591.

Quastler, H., Information theory (biological applications). In: *McGraw-Hill Encyclopedia of Science and Technology, 7:* 102–103.

Quastler, H., Information theory in biology. In: *Medical Physics* (O. Glasser, ed.), *5:* 294–299, Year Book, Chicago.

Sherman, F. G., and H. Quastler, DNA synthesis in irradiated intestinal epithelium, *Exptl. Cell Res., 19:* 343–360.

Wimber, D. E., H. Quastler, O. L. Stein, and D. R. Wimber, Analysis of tritium incorporation into individual cells by autoradiography of squash preparations, *J. Biophys. Biochem. Cytol., 8:* 327–331.

1961 Augenstine, L., and H. Quastler, Review of comparative effects of radiation, *Am. J. Human Genet., 13* (3): 351.

Cattaneo, S. M., H. Quastler, and F. G. Sherman, Proliferative cycle in the growing hair follicle of the mouse, *Nature, 190:* 923–924.

Dornfest, B. S., J. LoBue, A. S. Gordon, and H. Quastler, Leukocyte release from perfused isolated femurs of rats, *Federation Proc., 20* (*1, Pt. 1*): 71 (Abst.).

Hampton, J. C., and H. Quastler, Combined autoradiography and electron microscopy of thin sections of intestinal epithelial cells of the mouse labeled with H^3-thymidine, *J. Biophys. Biochem. Cytol., 10:* 140–144.

Lipkin, M., T. P. Almy, and H. Quastler, Stability of protein in intestinal epithelial cells, *Science, 133:* 1019–1021.

Lipkin, M., and H. Quastler, Cell population kinetics in the colon, *Federation Proc., 20* (*1, Pt. 1*): 242 (Abst.).

LoBue, J., B. S. Dornfest, A. S. Gordon, and H. Quastler, Marrow distribution in the rat femur as determined by Fe^{59} labeling, *Anat. Record, 139:* 313 (Abst.).

Perrotta, C. A., H. Quastler, and N. Staley, 1961. Proliferation in the vaginal epithelium of the mouse as shown by autoradiography with tritiated thymidine, *Anat. Record, 139:* 263–264 (Abst.).

Quastler, H., Time-dose relations in radiation effects. In: *Proc. Conf. Res. Radiotherapy of Cancer,* pp. 100–112.

Sherman, F. G., H. Quastler, and D. R. Wimber, Cell population kinetics in the ear epidermis of mice, *Exptl. Cell Res., 25:* 114–119.

Wulff, V. J., H. Quastler, and F. G. Sherman, The incorporation of H^3-cytidine in mice of different ages. *Arch. Biochem. Biophys. 95:* 548–549.

1962 Dornfest, B. S., J. LoBue, E. S. Handler, A. S. Gordon, and H. Quastler, Mechanisms of leukocyte production and release. I. Factors influencing leukocyte release from isolated perfused rat femora, *Acta Haematol., 28:* 42–60.

Dornfest, B. S., J. LoBue, E. S. Handler, A. S. Gordon, and H. Quastler, Mechanisms of leukocyte production and release. II. Factors influencing leukocyte release from isolated perfused rat legs, *J. Lab. Clin. Med., 60:* 777–787.

Kember, N. F., H. Quastler, and D. R. Wimber,

Adaptation of the rat intestine to continuous irradiation, *Brit. J. Radiol., 35:* 290.

Levy, C. K., and H. Quastler, Acute responses of the vestibular apparatus to x-irradiation, *Radiation Res., 16:* 189–200.

Lipkin, M., and H. Quastler, Cell population kinetics in the colon of the mouse, *J. Clin. Invest., 41:* 141–146.

Lipkin, M., and H. Quastler, Studies of protein metabolism in intestinal epithelial cells, *J. Clin. Invest., 41:* 646–653.

Lipkin, M. and H. Quastler, Cell retention and incidence of carcinoma in several portions of the gastrointestinal tract, *Nature, 194:* 1198–1199.

McCarter, J. A., and H. Quastler, Note on the effect of a carcinogenic hydrocarbon on the synthesis of deoxyribonucleic acid, *Biochim. Biophys. Acta, 55:* 552–553.

McCarter, J. A., and H. Quastler, Effect of dimethylbenzanthracene on the cellular proliferation cycle, *Nature, 194:* 873–874.

Quastler, H., and J. C. Hampton, Effects of ionizing radiation on the fine structure and function of the intestinal epithelium of the mouse. I. Villus Epithelium, *Radiation Res., 17:* 914–931.

Quastler, H., and G. Zubay, An RNA-protein code based on replacement data. II. Adjustment and extension, *J. Theoret. Biol., 3:* 496–502.

Stein, O. L., and H. Quastler, The effect of tritiated thymidine on the morphogenesis of lateral roots. In: *Tritium in the Physical and Biological Sciences, 2:* 149–153, *Intern. Atomic Energy Assoc.,* Vienna.

Wulff, V. J., H. Quastler, and F. G. Sherman, An hypothesis concerning RNA metabolism and aging, *Proc. Natl. Acad. Sci. U.S., 48:* 1373–1375.

Zubay, G., and H. Quastler, An RNA-protein code based on replacement data, *Proc. Natl. Acad. Sci. U.S. 48:* 461–471.

1963 Lamerton, L. F., B. I. Lord, and H. Quastler, Studies of cell population kinetics in normal and continuously irradiated animals. In: *Radioaktive Isotope in*

Klinik und Forschung (K. Fellinger and R. Höfer, eds.), p. 493–501, Urban and Schwarzenberg, Munich and Berlin.

Lipkin, M., H. Quastler, and F. Muggia, Protein synthesis in the irradiated intestine of the mouse, *Radiation Res., 19:* 277–285.

LoBue, J., B. S. Dornfest, A. S. Gordon, J. Hurst, and H. Quastler, Marrow distribution in rat femurs determined by cell enumeration and Fe^{59} labeling, *Proc. Soc. Exptl. Biol. Med., 112:* 1058–1062.

Patt, H. M., and H. Quastler, Radiation effects on cell renewal and related systems, *Physiol. Rev., 43:* 357–396.

Quastler, H., Chemical communication systems in the cell, *Trans. N.Y. Acad. Sci., 25:* 382–395.

Quastler, H., The analysis of cell population kinetics. In: *Cell Proliferation, A Guinness Symposium* (L. F. Lamerton and R. J. M. Fry, eds.), pp. 18–36, Blackwell, Oxford.

Quastler, H., Effects of irradiation on intestinal mucosal cell population, *Federation Proc., 22 (Pt. 1):* 1330–1333.

Quastler, H., Effects of irradiation on synthesis and loss of DNA. In: *Chemical and Biological Actions of Radiation* (M. Haïssinsky, ed.), pp. 149–185, Masson, Paris.

Stein, O. L., and H. Quastler, The use of tritiated thymidine in the study of tissue activation during germination in *Zea mays, Am. J. Botany, 50:* 1006–1011.

Wimber, D. E., and H. Quastler, A ^{14}C- and ^{3}H-thymidine double labeling technique in the study of cell proliferation in *Tradescantia* root tips, *Exptl. Cell Res., 30:* 8–22.

1964 Quastler, H., General principles of systems analysis. In: *Theoretical and Mathematical Biology* (T. H. Waterman and H. J. Morowitz, eds.), Blaisdell, New York (in press).

Index

Bold face page numbers indicate location of references. Italic page numbers refer to figures.